A Guide to Teaching Circuits

David Lee

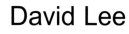

Published by Amacsports Limited.

Amacsports
PO Box 2
Adisham
Canterbury
CT3 3XR
Published 2004

British Library cataloguing in Publication Data

A CIP record for this book is available from the British library.

ISBN   0-9540695-8-7

DISCLAIMER

The author and publisher of the book are not responsible for any injury which may result from following the instructions within.

Before embarking on any of the physical activities described in this book, the reader should consult his/her doctor for advice regarding their individual suitability for performing such activity.

All activities in this book should be performed under the supervision of a qualified instructor.

Printed in Great Britain

CONTENTS

CIRCUIT TRAINING

Circuit training involves a number of different activities or stations which can be arranged to develop general fitness or specific components of fitness. Circuit training offers many advantages:

1. It is very flexible - the circuit can be easily manipulated to concentrate on different fitness components (for example, muscular strength and endurance, aerobic endurance, power, speed, agility, and so on …) by choosing appropriate exercises;

2. Circuit training can help to improve the development of skills and improve sports performance;

3. It can cater for all ability levels and for large numbers of participants (encouraging social interaction);

4. Circuit training can help with weight management;

5. Progression can be built into the circuits as fitness levels improve;

6. Circuits are easily adapted and there are countless variations in the choice of exercises and equipment that can be used;

7. Circuit training is a safe, effective and fun way of exercising and can be performed by all.

PLANNING A PROGRAMME OF CIRCUIT TRAINING SESSIONS

It is unlikely that you will deliver one-off circuit training sessions to different participants. It is far more likely that you will deliver your circuit classes as part of a continuous programme with regular participants attending. This may be in a sports or fitness setting - at a sports or martial arts club - to improve the fitness of those taking part, or in a health/fitness centre or gym as part of the range of classes offered to their members.

Wherever possible, each individual circuit training session should be part of a programme or series of sessions. You need to identify appropriate goals for the whole series of sessions, as well as specific and progressive goals for each individual session. You must identify fixed points in the programme. Fixed points are 'key' or significant events within your sport/training. Examples may include specific competitions, gradings or assessments, the length of a season, and lifestyle events such as going on holiday. These are easily defined points in the participants programme.

At all times ensure that the principles of training (i.e. overload, progression and specificity) are being applied to the plan, the planned development of each component matches its priority, and the programme is developed with due consideration for the identified fixed points.

You must agree the programme with others. These other people may include parents/guardians, other coaches or teachers, support personnel and the participants themselves.

Once you have planned the programme and it has been agreed by all concerned, you must ensure that it is fully documented, with written contingencies for participants who do not achieve their goals and for when sessions do not go according to plan.

The resources necessary to implement the planned programme should be identified before commencing running the sessions. Negotiate the availability of resources with the centre or other teachers/instructors and ensure the resources are within the program's budget. The plan should be modified to match the available resources and financial availability where necessary and should be fully documented.

PLANNING A PROGRESSIVE PROGRAMME

It is important to plan the progression of your sessions in order to improve the fitness of your participants. The **F.I.T.T. principle** can be used to help you.

F: **FREQUENCY** - Increase the number of sessions per week.

I: **INTENSITY** - Make the exercises harder. This can be achieved by:
a. Increasing the length of a lever to increase body weight, e.g. box press ups, to extended box press ups, to normal press ups, to raised leg press ups.
b. Move the arms or external resistance further from the pivot point, e.g. perform the ab curl with hands on thighs (easiest), hands across chest, hands by head, arms extended behind head, arms extended behind head holding a weight (hardest). The pivot point in the ab curl is the lumbar spine (lower back).
c. Increasing the range of movement, e.g. partial squat to full squat (90°).
d. Increasing the speed at which the exercise is performed (while maintaining correct technique).
e. By using external resistance, e.g. performing the lunge without weights (easiest) to the lunge with weights (harder). The heavier the weight the more intense the exercise.

T: **TIME** - Progression can occur in the following ways:
a. Increase the work to rest ratio, i.e. increase the amount of time spent exercising or the number of repetitions performed at each station, and/or decrease the amount of rest time between each station. More work is carried out in the session, although the length of the session does not alter.
b. Lengthen the session. This can be achieved by introducing more stations or by going round the stations 2 or more times.

T: **TYPE** - Introduce more complicated exercises, which are more challenging and involve more than one muscle group, i.e. in the early stages incorporate simple isolation exercises (one muscle group), and gradually incorporate compound exercises (working more than one muscle group). This will help maintain interest and avoid boredom.

CHECKLIST FOR PLANNING A CIRCUIT TRAINING SESSION

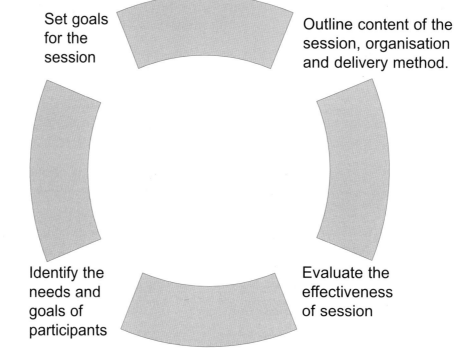

Set goals for the session

Outline content of the session, organisation and delivery method.

Identify the needs and goals of participants

Evaluate the effectiveness of session

Careful planning of each session and a long-term scheme which takes into account how to progressively improve the fitness of your participants will ensure that each session is properly structured and will run smoothly. Time spent on planning and preparation is always time well spent, and should involve gathering as much information as possible, before setting aims and objectives and choosing activities and equipment.

Identify the short term goals that each session will contribute to, and make sure that they are consistent with the goals of the training cycle and programme. An outline plan should be produced for each session and make sure that the plan contributes to the identified short term goals. Plans should always conform to health and safety requirements

You should make sure that the plan maximises the time and resources available, and that methods of delivery are appropriate to the sport/activity, participants, and resources. Contingency plans should be developed for participants who do not achieve the goals of the session, and agree the plan with others. Document the agreed plan and contingencies for the session.

All planning should be done well in advance and you should make sure that the information you collect to plan your sessions is relevant, complete, up-to-date and accurate. The activities should be planned so that they meet the overall aims of the session, the training cycle, the season and the programme, as well as meeting the needs of individual participants.

Below are some questions which need to be asked regarding the circuit training session you will be delivering:

1.*How many participants will you have in your circuit?*
    -Make sure you have enough stations and enough space for the participants at each.
    -This may determine what layout of circuit to use and how much equipment is needed.
    -What is the average age and overall age range of those taking part in your circuit?
    -Are there any special needs for those taking part?
    -Are there any medical conditions or injuries for any participant taking part in the session?
    -If yes, what affect will it have on their ability to exercise? What affect will exercise have on their condition?
    -Are they on medication for their condition or injury?
    -If yes, what is the affect of the medication on exercise, and what affect does exercise have on the medication?
    -The above information will help to make sure that all activities and exercises are safe and suitable for those taking part in this circuit training session.

2.*The standard of fitness of those participating in your circuit.*
    -Are they all of the same ability or are they of mixed ability?
    -If participants are of mixed ability, how are you going to modify or adapt the exercises/activities to ensure everyone can participate and no one is excluded?
    -Are there alternative exercises or activities that may be more appropriate?
    -The participants' fitness level determines which exercises and activities to include in the circuit.

3.*The level of skill of those participating in your circuit.*
    -Are the participants' beginners, intermediates or advanced in terms of their skill?
    -How will you organise mixed ability groups?

4.*How will you manage/organise your circuit/group?*
    -What type and layout of circuit will you use?

-How are you going to get their attention during the session?

-How are you going to position the participants so they can all see you demonstrate?

5.*Check the following for the suitability of your premises:*
   -Is there sufficient space?
   -Is the surface okay? i.e. dry, free from debris, clean, no holes!
   -Ventilation, lighting, heating, first aid kit, toilets, showers, drinking water - all okay or available?
   -Are fire exits clear of obstruction?
   -Are the facilities safe and suitable for the circuit?
   -Do they need to be booked?

6.*What are the aims/goals of your circuit? For example, to develop muscular endurance and aerobic endurance; to develop speed and power, etc.*
   -You need to take into account the overall goals for the training cycle, season and programme.
   -Are these aims or goals new to the participants?
   -How will you link these into previous sessions and learning?
   -Has your session plan clear objectives (what the participants will be able to do)?

7.*What are the aims and needs of those taking part? For example, to lose weight, to improve performance in their sport, to improve general fitness, etc.*
   -Have you accurately identified the participants' needs?
   -Are any of the participants' needs going to conflict with the aims of the programme?
   -Will the participants' needs be met through this session?

8.*Are the sequences of activities/exercises and timings realistic for the participants?*
   -For example, overloading the same muscle group in sequential exercises may be suitable for the well trained athlete; but may be, however, far too much for a beginner.

9.*Do you have any evaluations from previous sessions?*
   -These will help you to identify what worked in previous sessions and what you did well.
   -Action points resulting from identified weaknesses also need to be addressed.
   -Were there any activities or exercises that were particularly liked or disliked?

10.*How much time is available for your circuit?*
   -How long has been allocated for warming up, the main activity and cooling down?

11.*What equipment is needed for your circuit?*
   -Is it available?
   -Do you need to book it?
   -Check the equipment is safe and suitable for your circuit and the participants taking part.

12.*How long will the participants perform each exercise and how long will they rest between stations?*
   -Allow enough time for recovery between stations.

13.*Do you want or need music?*
   -Is it suitable for your circuit?
   -Music can help motivate the participants.

14.*How will you deal with the 'what ifs'? i.e. what are your contingencies?*
   -What if odd numbers turn up?

-What if more participants turn up for the session than is planned for?
-What if fewer participants turn up for the session than is planned for?
-What if the participants cannot grasp the basics?
-What if someone is injured or hurts themselves?
-What if an activity or exercise proves to be unpopular or too difficult?
-What if an activity or exercise proves to be too easy or boring?
-What if some of the participants understand and perform the activity or exercise, whilst others in the group do not?
-What if the training environment is too hot or too cold?
-What if the session plans are clearly not working? Will you be willing (or prepared) to change them?

15. *Does your plan meet organisational and legal health and safety requirements?*
-Do your participants know the risks involved with the activities and the exercises? Make sure they know what they are and how to minimise them.
-Make sure you provide a safe environment.
-Provide safe equipment for the participants.
-Make sure that the circuit training session is supervised at all times. Circumstances can very quickly change that can affect the safety of the participants.
-Always warm up and cool down the participants.
-Make sure that all clothing and footwear (for both you and the participants) is safe and suitable for the activities and exercises within the circuit training session.
-If you are pairing anyone for an activity within your session, make sure they are matched according to height, weight, ability and experience.

16. *Does your understanding of what is planned and your own personal competence and qualifications meet the requirements of leading the session?*
-Do you need to obtain further skills or knowledge?
-Do you need to use others' expertise? i.e. do you need to get help from somebody more qualified and experienced, or a specialist?

EXERCISE SUITABILITY & CIRCUIT LAYOUT

Exercises must be selected and arranged so that the overload principle applies, sufficient recovery is catered for and all factors of fitness are considered. The principle of circuit training is that the participant works at sub-maximum level over a period of time with either no rest, or minimal rest between exercises.

The whole musculature of the body should be exercised. The exercises used must give a balanced loading on different body parts, with no one muscle group being exercised in consecutive stations; this allows an active recovery of the muscle group(s) involved whilst maintaining the work load. Throughout the circuit, the exercises should be varied enough to cover the full range of movement for that particular group of muscles (e.g. for the quadriceps or thighs - squats, step ups, lunges, knee raises, leg extensions and so on).

The easiest way of organising the exercise stations in your circuit is in the form of a circle or rectangle, starting at one station and then working around the circle until the starting point is reached again.

A "B.A.L.S" approach is often recommended (alternating Back, Arm, Leg and Stomach exercises).

It is your responsibility to ensure that all the equipment is in safe working order. A check should be made to see that the equipment has been assembled correctly and is in the correct position. Unsafe equipment should be removed.

Ensure that there is a sufficient space between the stations and for any other form of activity that will be used in the circuit, e.g. shuttle or agility runs. Also, when there are large numbers of participants, it is important to make sure that there is sufficient space and equipment at each station to allow for the safe performance of participants exercising there.

Every participant should be totally familiar with all exercises used in the circuit. If participants are not clear about any exercise or activity, ensure that they receive a clear demonstration with all coaching and safety points, and are given time to rehearse the exercise. Correct execution is very important, and quality of performance, rather than quantity (i.e. number of repetitions) should be stressed at all times.

ADAPTATION OF EXERCISES OR PROGRAMMES

Thorough planning, effective communication, control and organisation will normally ensure the successful delivery of the circuit training session. However, there are occasions where the instructor has to improvise - respond to changes to their plans.

Some activities or exercises may not be appropriate for a participant or a given circumstance so you must have the ability to change or modify an exercise to make it appropriate for them. Factors which may involve adaptation of exercises include:

1.More or less participants attend your session. With too many participants, there may not be enough equipment for everyone using the circuit you had planned. There may also not be enough space for the participants to train safely and effectively. With too few participants, you may find that there is not enough people to form groups or pairs of similar ability and fitness levels (depending on the type of circuit used.)

2.The environment - The temperature of the hall may result in the circuit content having to be adapted. If it is too cold, a more vigorous or intense session than the one planned may be necessary. Poor ventilation resulting in the hall being too hot may result in the exercise intensity having to be reduced to prevent overheating. A slippery floor surface may prove dangerous for some dynamic activities, and more static exercises may be more appropriate to ensure safety.

3.Ability or fitness levels - Some exercises may need to be modified for certain participants to ensure that they are performing according to their present ability or fitness level. A beginner may not be able to safely perform certain exercises, and easier variations should be given.

4.Injury or weakness - If a person has an injury or has a certain weakness in a joint or muscle group, it may be possible to modify the position in which an exercise might normally be performed.

5.Enjoyment - if the participants are finding the circuit training session extremely boring and repetitive, it may be necessary to improvise and introduce some new activities.

APPROACHES TO CIRCUIT TRAINING

There are a number of different approaches to circuit training, all of which can be modified and adapted to emphasise different components of fitness and meet the needs of the participants and the training environment. The most common approaches have been listed below:

1.**TIMED CIRCUITS** - The participants are given a set work time at each exercise station (usually 15 seconds to 1 minute) immediately followed by a set rest period (depending on the participants' fitness level and the training goal of the session). Participants change stations when their work period is completed. The longer the work time and the shorter the rest time - the harder the circuit. In contrast, to make the circuit easier, either decrease the work time, increase the rest time, or both.

2.**REPETITION CIRCUITS** - A range of repetitions for each exercise is set out and graded according to difficulty. As soon as the designated number of repetitions has been achieved, the participant moves on to the next station. For example, participants at each station have a choice of 10, 20, or 30 repetitions depending on their ability and fitness levels. Make sure that you provide enough equipment and allow enough space between stations to prevent overcrowding or queuing.

3.**AEROBIC CIRCUITS** - Rhythmic exercises which use the large, major muscle groups are used in this type of circuit. Movement is continuous, with no or minimal rest between exercise stations. There is a wide range of cardiovascular equipment that could be used in this type of circuit.

4.**MSE CIRCUITS** - This type of circuit aims to improve muscular strength and endurance. The exercises can use the weight of the body as the resistance, dumbbells, barbells, bodybars, rubbers/tubing, fixed resistance machines, medicine balls, and so on. The NSCA recommend the following sets, reps and rest periods:

Training Goal		Goal Repetitions	Sets	Rest period length
Strength		<=6	2-6	2-5 min
Power	Single-effort event	1-2	2-5 min	2-5 min
	Multiple-effort event	3-5	2-5 min	2-5 min
Hypertrophy (bigger muscles)		6-12	3-6	30 sec-1.5 min
Muscular endurance		>=12	2-3	<= 30 sec

5. **COMBINATION CIRCUITS** - This type of circuit is a combination of the aerobic and MSE circuits outlined above. It aims to improve aerobic fitness and muscular strength and endurance. Although this type of circuit requires good organisation and group management skills, it is an excellent way of developing fitness.

6. **CONTINUOUS CIRCUITS** - In this type of circuit, the aim is to keep the movement constant, with no (or minimal) rest periods. It's aims are to develop aerobic endurance and the circuit may sometimes resemble an obstacle course or take the form of a series of lines rather than the traditional square or circle.

7. **COMMAND CIRCUITS** - In this type of circuit, all exercises are performed on the teacher's command - they give the commands for when "stops" or "starts" are to take place, or how many repetitions are to be performed. Although large numbers of participants can train at the same time, this type of circuit tends to feel quite regimented and it may prove difficult to correct individuals.

8. **SPORT SPECIFIC CIRCUITS** - This type of circuit aims to prepare individuals and improve performance in a particular sport. It uses exercises that are specific to the sport. When you design a sport-specific circuit the following principles must be observed:

a.Emphasise the same muscles that the sport most commonly uses but ensure a balanced whole body approach is adopted.

b.Emphasise the main energy systems that are used in the sport.

c.Use exercises that imitate the movements of the sport, working the joints through the specific angles and ranges that are necessary for the sport.

d.Work for the same duration and at the same intensity demanded by the sport.

LAYOUT OF CIRCUIT STATIONS

There are many different ways of laying out a circuit. The layout needs to be suitable for the number of participants and the activities being performed. A number of different layouts have been outlined below:

a) Traditional Squares

This circuit layout allows a large number and variety of exercises and activities to be performed.

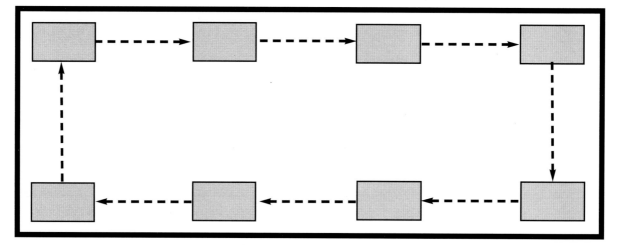

For example, an MSE traditional squares circuit:

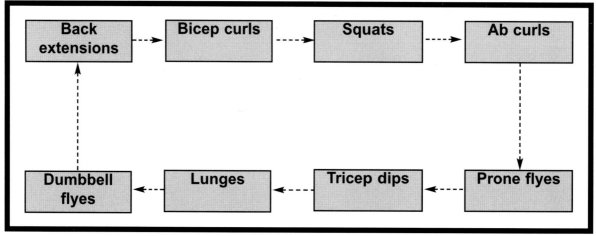

1 minute per station
20 seconds rest in between each station

b) Sets Circuit

This type of circuit is a variation of the Traditional Squares format. Each exercise or activity station requires completion of 2 to 3 sets before moving onto the next exercise station. There is a rest between each set and between each exercise. An example is shown below

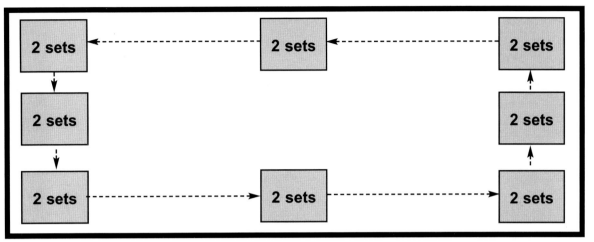

For example, an MSE sets circuit

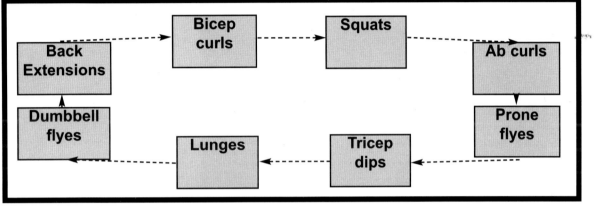

2 sets of 12 reps at each station
30 seconds rest between sets and between stations

c) Supersets Circuit

This type of circuit is a variation of the above sets format. Each exercise or activity station requires completion of 2 to 3 sets of two different exercises before moving onto the next exercise station. The two exercises at each station work opposing muscle groups so there is no need for rest between each set and between each exercise. For example, a station might consist of ab curls and back extensions, or tricep dips and bicep curls. An example is shown below:

For example, an MSE supersets circuit:

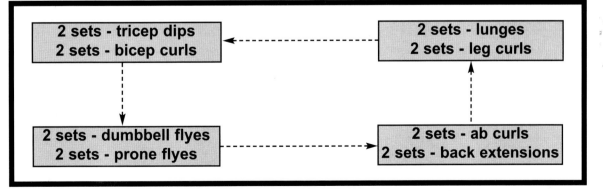

2 sets of 15 reps of each exercise at each station
(e.g. 1 set lunges, 1 set leg curls, 1 set lunges, 1 set leg curls … next station)
Minimal rest between sets, exercises and stations

d) Lines

This circuit layout is excellent for cardiovascular workouts. It involves organising the participants into lines. Each row in the line is a different exercise station.

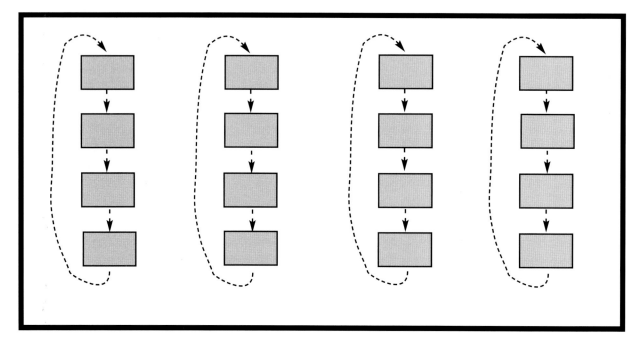

For example, an aerobic lines circuit:

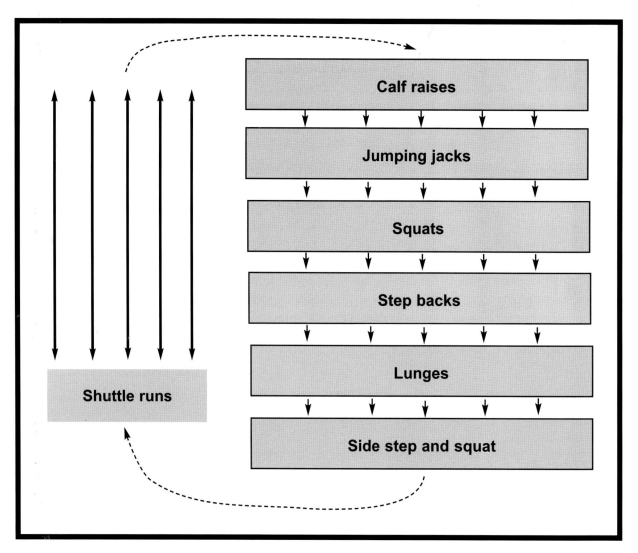

e) Corners

With this circuit layout, the training hall has an exercise or activity in each corner. The participants complete the circuit at least twice.

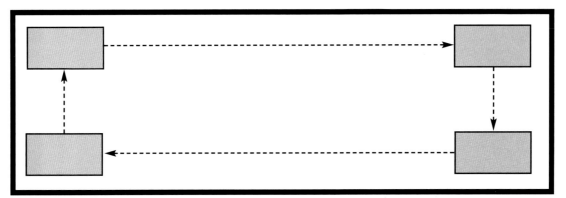

For example, an MSE corners circuit:

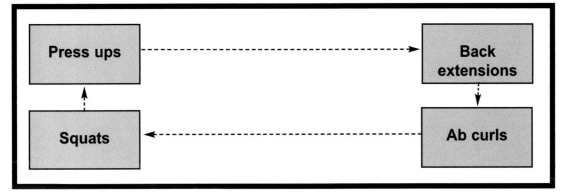

1 minute per station
30 seconds rest between each station

Another example, a plyometric corner circuit:

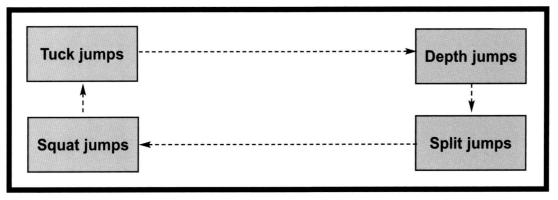

5 repetitions per station
2 minutes active recovery between stations

f) Shuttles

This circuit layout is very good for improving aerobic fitness. The training hall is divided into sections as shown in the diagram below. Each line represents a different exercise. The participants run to the first line, perform the first exercise and then run back to the starting line. They then run to the second line, perform the second exercise and then run back to the starting line. This is repeated until the whole circuit has been completed.

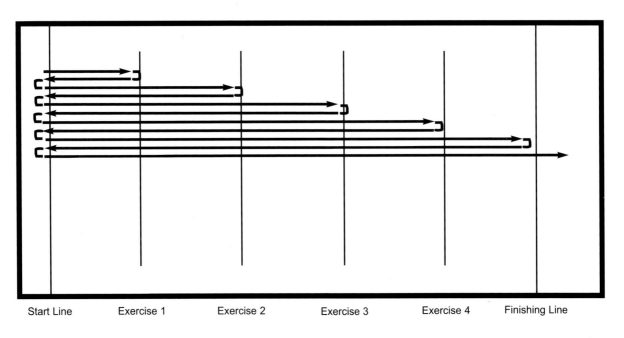

Start Line   Exercise 1   Exercise 2   Exercise 3   Exercise 4   Finishing Line

For example, an MSE shuttle circuit:

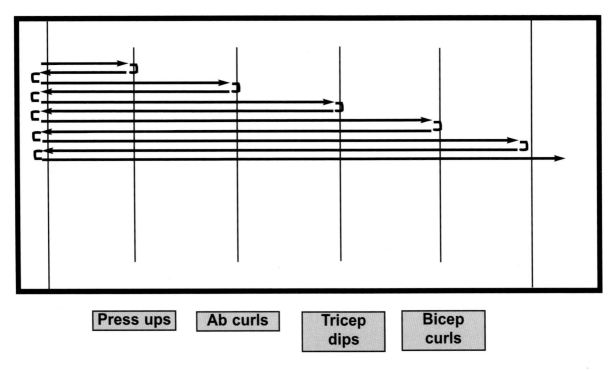

Press ups   **Ab curls**   **Tricep dips**   **Bicep curls**

20 repetitions at each station
No rest between stations

g) Duplication

Participants of similar abilities are paired together. The equipment needed is duplicated at each station. Each participant competes simultaneously against their partner in how many repetitions are achieved in the set time limit for each station.

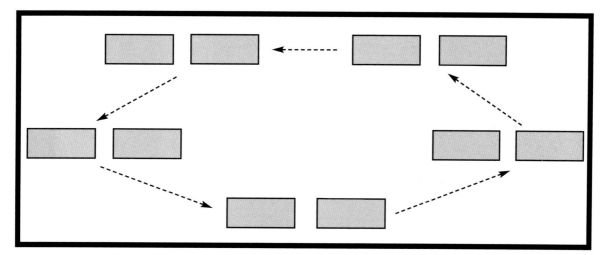

For example, an MSE duplication circuit:

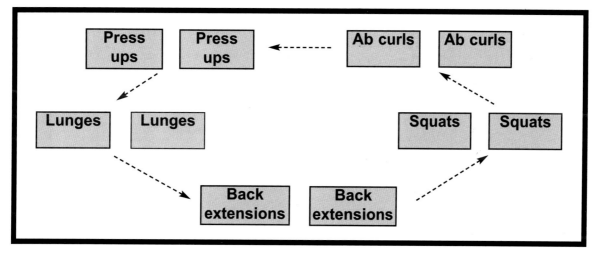

1 minute per station
30 seconds rest in between each station

h) Triplication

Three sets of equipment are laid out at each station - hard/moderate/easy. Each participant follows the circuit round selecting their own intensity of work, e.g. have dumbbells at 5kg, 10kg, and 15kg.

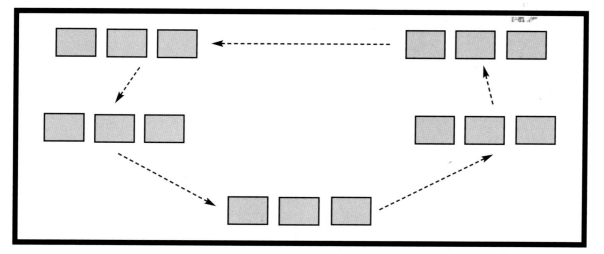

i) Triangles

This circuit consists of 2 or 3 triangles (3 exercises per triangle). The triangles are made up of exercises for one muscle group, e.g. 3 different abdominal exercises, then 3 chest exercises, followed by 3 leg exercises.

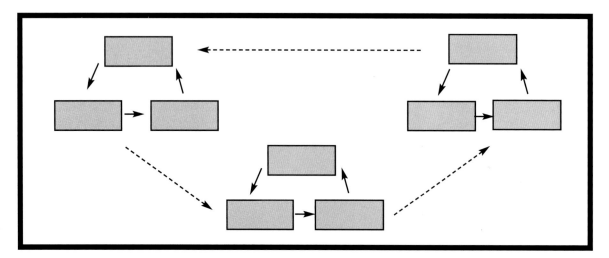

For example, an MSE triangles circuit:

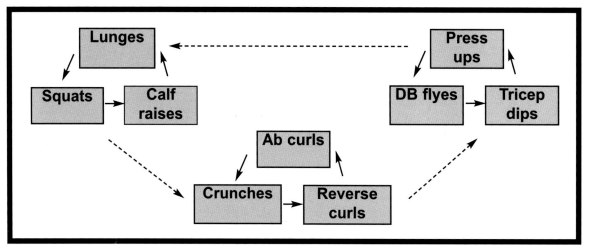

15 repetitions per station
30 seconds rest in between stations

j) Squares

This circuit consists of 2 or 3 squares (4 exercises per square). The squares are made up of exercises for one muscle group, e.g. 4 different abdominal exercises, then 4 chest exercises, followed by 4 leg exercises.

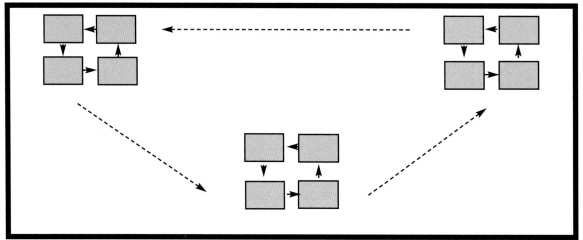

k) Split Half

The participants are split into two groups. Each group is directed to one half of the training hall. A list at the front of the class of the exercises to be completed may be of help. One group performs one exercise while the other group performs a different one. This layout is excellent for developing aerobic fitness and is easier to manage than other layouts.

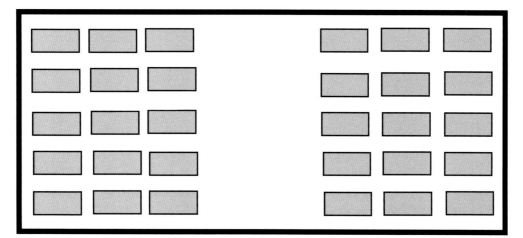

l) Recorded Circuit

Each participant records the maximum number of repetitions completed in the time limit. Participants who follow attempt to beat the maximum recorded. Remember to place a pen and paper at each station. This type of circuit can be used with most layouts.

m) Star Circuit

This is when each participant runs to the centre of the circuit and performs some type of exercise between each station, e.g. 10 ab curls between each station. Ensure that this exercise is not placed within the circuit.

For example, an MSE star circuit:

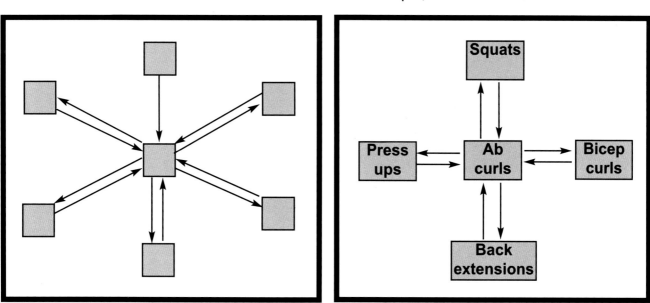

1 minute per station
Minimal rest between stations

n) Overtaking Circuit

Participants start off at different stations and attempt to overtake the person in front of them. This type of circuit can be used with most layouts, but is best used with a repetition based circuit (rather than timed). Make sure that in their attempts to overtake, they do not sacrifice good technique for speed. It is inadvisable to use this circuit with beginners until they can perform each exercise safely and effectively.

o) Team Circuit

Divide the class into teams of similar ability. One team starts the first station, whilst the other teams wait in line. Once the first team has moved to the second station, the next team starts, trying to better the time or reps of the first team. This procedure continues until all teams have finished.

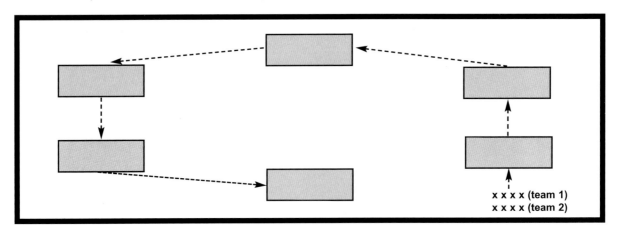

p) Team line Circuit

Divide the class into teams. All participants line up in their teams at one side of training hall. All stations are in a line in front of each team. Teams move on to the next station when the whole team has finished. (Teams must be of similar ability).

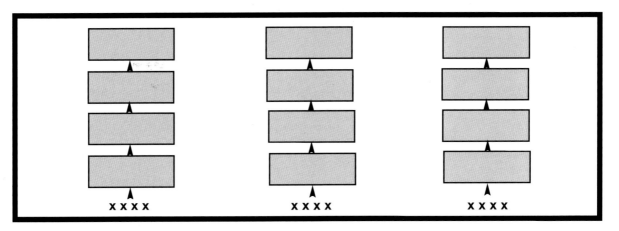

q) Partner Timed Circuit

Participants of similar ability are paired together. Each pair start at different stations in the circuit. One of the pair performs the exercise, whilst the partner runs around the perimeter of the circuit. When the runner returns, the pair switch places. They move onto the next station when both have run around the outside.

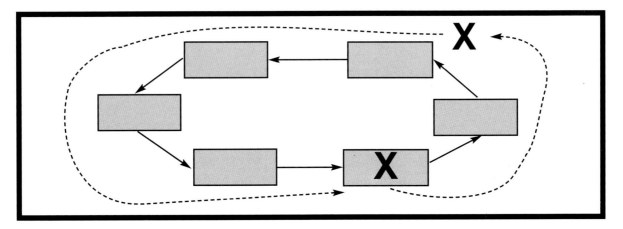

r) Obstacle Circuit

This type of circuit is continuous and is basically an obstacle course. Various pieces of equipment are laid out to form a continuous circuit and may include benches, mats, steps, gymnastic equipment, ladders and hurdles. It is inadvisable to use this circuit with beginners. For example:

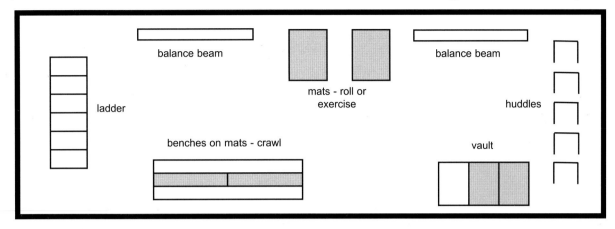

s) Potted Sports Circuit

This type of circuit encourages the learning of sports skills. The circuit can be sport-specific (i.e. skills from one particular sport) or general in nature (general skills from many different sports). This type of circuit is excellent for beginners who want to improve their skills and for intermediate or advanced participants who want to have fun and improve their fitness and skills. An example of a sport specific potted sports circuit can be found below. This is a combat circuit for developing skills in martial arts (see 101 Games and Drills for Martial Arts for further examples of games or drills that can be used in a combat circuit):

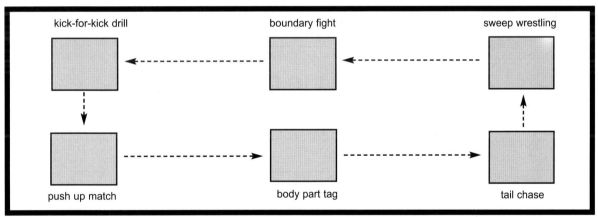

Below you will find an example of a general potted sports circuit:

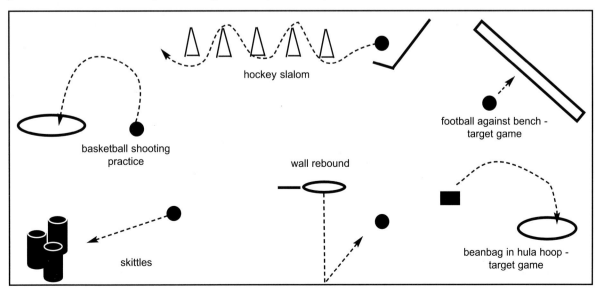

WARMING UP

It is extremely important that you thoroughly warm up the participants at the start of every circuit training session. An effective warm up prepares each participant physically and mentally for the activities and exercise to come.

Warm ups are essential for helping to prevent injuries by raising the temperature of the muscles, and gently stretching the muscles, ligaments, tendons and connective tissues. Warm ups also help to improve the body's efficiency for the activity to come by increasing heart rate, respiratory rate and metabolism. Warm ups also enable the participants to practise and improve technical performance for the activity to come.

Some general guidelines for warm ups are outlined below:
- Joints should be gently mobilised by taking each one slowly through its range of movement.
- Whole body movements using continuous, rhythmic motions and large muscle groups should be employed to raise the temperature of the body. These should gradually increase in intensity.
- Muscles and connective tissue should then be gently stretched.
- The body should be re-warmed after the stretch using activities or exercises that are directly related to those in the main body of the circuit.
- The warm up should work each participant at an appropriate intensity without any undue fatigue resulting.
- Activities or exercises used within the warm up may have to be adapted to suit the fitness and ability of individual participants.
- There should be a minimal timelag between the end of the warm up and the start of the main part of the circuit.

COOLING DOWN

At the end of a circuit training session, it is important that you lead a safe and effective cool down. This needs to be done to return bodies back down to pre-exercise levels.

This is carried out by performing whole body movements using continuous, rhythmic motions and large muscle groups to gradually lower the temperature of the body. This is then followed by stretches which need to be held for at least 30 seconds in order to develop flexibility.

TEACHING CIRCUITS

Introducing and Explaining Techniques
A good introduction gives participants a good general idea of how the activity or exercise is to be performed.

Organising participants for the introduction
- Get their attention and organise them so they can see and hear.
- Position the participant(s) so that the background is free from visual distractions.
- Select an area free of excessive background noise (if possible).

Delivering the introduction
- Tell the participants what they are learning and why it is important.
- The introduction should be kept brief, simple and direct.
- Pay particular attention to the language used - it should be appropriate to the participant.
- Avoid using technical words and jargon.
- K.I.S.S (keep it short and simple).

Preparing the explanation

- An effective explanation needs to be planned - select the best words.
- Literal explanations state literally what should be done - most participants find this type of explanation far too detailed and complicated.
- Figurative explanations use an example or an image to describe the technique.
- In many cases, a combination of both literal and figurative explanations may be best.
- Relate the technique to previous ones the participant has learned - transfer of learning.
- Verbal pretraining can improve the teaching of complex techniques - supply simple word labels to help remind what to do next.
- These labels identify the steps in the sequence simply and directly, making the teaching and learning of techniques much easier. For example, 'hop', 'skip' and 'jump' for the three steps of the triple jump.
- Verbal pretraining should be part of the explanation.
- Demonstrate the sequence as you describe the labels.
- Make sure that labels are simple and direct and describe the technique to be learned.

Delivering the explanation

- Use language that is appropriate for the participant and free of jargon.
- Keep it brief, simple and direct.
- State how the demonstration will proceed.
- Identify a few of the most relevant cues for the technique.
- It may be useful to divide the exercise technique into three stages:
  - Set up and preparation;
  - Action;
  - Finish.
- Try to include at least one relevant cue for each part.

Demonstrating Techniques

- A picture is worth a thousand words.
- The best way to supplement the introduction and explanation is to provide a demonstration of the technique.
- This acts as a model to copy.

How demonstrations work

- Learning from demonstrations involves four steps:
  - Attention;
  - Retention;
  - Reproduction;
  - Motivation.

- *Attention* - If not paying attention, participants will not know how to perform the technique.
  - Introduce the technique effectively.
  - Relevant cues to direct attention - without this, attention may be paid to inappropriate actions.

- *Retention* - If relevant cues cannot be remembered, participants will not be able to perform them.
  - Carefully selecting and demonstrating cues will aid retention.
  - Repeat the same cues with each demonstration.
  - Ask the participant to repeat back the teaching points/cues after the explanation and demonstration.
- Help the participant to reproduce the technique by following a logical progression of skills to allow the participant to experience success from the very beginning.

•Make sure the participant understands and can perform the basics at each step.
•Do not introduce more advanced techniques until easier ones have been mastered.
•Give the participant consistent and constructive feedback that will help them to learn and refine each technique.
•Motivation is important to learn the new skill.

In summary:
•Get the participant's attention;
•Direct the participant's attention to key movements;
•Repeat important cues/teaching points;
•Organise the demonstrations progressively to help the participant develop the movements;
•Motivate the participant to want to learn the new technique.

When to use demonstrations
•*Demonstrate before practice*
-Precede any attempts at practicing any new techniques with a demonstration.
-Several repetitions of the demonstration may be necessary to reinforce the technique.
-Demonstrate the technique from a variety of angles (or reposition the participant).
-If repeating techniques from a previous session, precede each one with a demonstration to help the participant remember the technique.

•*Demonstrations during practice.*
-Stop practices of new skills on occasion to repeat demonstrations - especially for participants who are making mistakes or for exercises that are very complex.
-If working with several participants and a few of them are all making the same mistake, organise a demonstration focusing on eliminating this mistake.

•*Demonstrate after practice.*
-After the participant has finished practising, a final demonstration may help to reinforce their mental picture of the technique.

Arranging participant(s) for demonstrations
•Make sure that all participants can see the demonstration.
•Ask participants to move to where they can see.
•Demonstrate the technique from various angles.
•If the exercise cannot be demonstrated from different angles, reposition the participants around the machine.
•Use mirrors. If looking in the mirror at the technique during the demonstration, participants can see the exercise from a different angle - this may reduce the number of demonstrations or repositioning of participants.

Who should demonstrate?
•The instructor or teacher.
•Poor demonstrations may reduce the participant's confidence in them.
•In some instances, for example in a circuit environment, it may be appropriate for a participant to demonstrate (providing they have good technique).

How often should the technique be demonstrated?
•Depends on the complexity of the technique and the ability or training status of the participant(s).
•Simple techniques may require only one or two demonstrations, whereas a more complex technique will require several demonstrations of the whole exercise as well as its parts.
•It is better to give too many demonstrations than too few.

Practising Techniques

- Identify aspects of the technique the participant is performing correctly.
- Identify aspects of the technique the participant is performing incorrectly.
- Analyse the cause of the mistakes.
- Work out what you will say to the participant when making corrections.
- Focus on only one or two mistakes at any one time to correct.
- Stop the practice and get the participant's attention.

Repeat the teaching

- Provide feedback to the participant after stopping practice and getting the participant's attention. Complement the participant for their effort and good technical points, and also give them plenty of encouragement. Explain and demonstrate how to correct any mistakes they may have made.
- *Repeat the explanation and demonstration* if they are still having difficulty with the technique. It may be necessary to demonstrate at a slower speed or stop at critical points to emphasise certain teaching points.
- *Check the participant understands.* This may be done by getting them to repeat the teaching points back, or by the instructor questioning them.
- *Let the participant practice the technique again.* If there are still mistakes or very little improvement then it may be necessary for the instructor to repeat the above stages, or it may be necessary to use a completely different strategy altogether. It may be that the exercise is too complex for the participant and an alternative may be more appropriate.

Part Methods

- Teaching a complex skill in its entirety may be too complex for some participants.
- Breaking down the exercise into smaller parts and teaching each part separately can often help.
- Demonstrate and explain the first part of the exercise and let the participant practice.
- If they are successful, let the participant practice the previous part and then demonstrate and explain the next part.
- Carry on in this way, so the participant experiences success for each individual part, gradually building up the whole technique.

Guidance Techniques

- *Visual guidance* involves the participant seeing what they have to do. Go through the technique step-by-step and as slowly as possible while the participant also performs the technique. It is important that feedback is given and any mistakes are corrected. It is important that the participant has a clear view.
- *Verbal guidance* involves the participant hearing what they have to do. Provide a label for each part of the technique. The instructor must also observe and provide feedback to the participant throughout.
- *Verbal and visual guidance* involves demonstration of the skill with labels describing the movement.
- *Manual guidance* involves taking control of the technique and doing some (or most) of the work for the participant. The participant is taken through the desired range of movement and should concentrate on what the movement feels like and the position of their limbs and angle of joints. Only use manual guidance for a few repetitions so that the participant can perform the correct technique unaided.

Feedback For Techniques

•The information a participant receives about their performance of an exercise is known as feedback.

•Systematic learning is impossible without learning.

•There are two major types of feedback:

•**Intrinsic (internal) feedback** is the information a participant receives as a natural consequence of performing an exercise. It involves how the movement felt, as well as what they heard, saw, and experienced through their senses. This feedback is produced by the participant him/herself.

•**Extrinsic (external) feedback** is produced by an external source such as the instructor, a friend, or a video of their performance. Extrinsic feedback can be given verbally or nonverbally

Feedback serves three important functions:

1.Information to correct mistakes with performance

-This type of feedback usually informs the participant about one or more of the following:

-Knowledge of results - the outcome of the performance - was it successful?

-Knowledge of performance - what parts of the technique were performed correctly and incorrectly.

-Kinaesthetic feedback - this concerns the way the movements felt whilst performing the exercise.

-Reasons for the mistake(s).

-Technical changes that need to be made to correct mistakes.

-Reasons why these technical changes were recommended.

Give this type of feedback to inform the participant about their performance. This feedback should provide specific information on how to correct mistakes and to reinforce correct technique.

Do not make comments that are loaded with judgment. Comments that are high in judgment and low in information have little, if any, impact on learning, but may have a tremendous impact on a participant's confidence or motivation.

Using extrinsic feedback as a source of information to correct mistakes should be given every time the participant performs the technique correctly or as frequently as possible in the participant's early stages of learning techniques. This will help to guide the participant toward performing the techniques correctly in less time than if feedback were given infrequently. It also increases the likelihood that the technique will be correct from the outset of learning.

As learning progresses and performance of the techniques improve, extrinsic feedback of this type should be gradually reduced so the participant gradually learns to become less dependent on it to perform the technique successfully.

2.Reinforcement to strengthen correct performance

-This type of feedback acts as reinforcement, strengthening the response the instructor wants the participant to learn. This type of reinforcement can either be positive or negative:

-Feedback that acts as **positive reinforcement** is pleasurable in some way to the participant who wants to experience this positive event again. For feedback to act as positive reinforcement, it must immediately follow the action to increase the chances of this action occurring again under the same or similar conditions.

-This type of feedback may be intrinsic in nature and may be connected with a feeling of achievement, accomplishment or success.

-This type of feedback can also be extrinsic in nature - verbal complements or praise from the instructor (or a friend, training partner, family member, etc), or nonverbal forms of communication (for example, a smile, a nod, thumbs up, etc). A participant receiving this type of feedback immediately after successfully performing an exercise can feel much rewarded by their success.

-To obtain this feeling again, the participant will try to perform the same technique in the same way in the future under similar conditions.

-What appears to be positive reinforcement to one participant can be seen as entirely some thing else by another. Instructors should be aware that positive reinforcement, although a very powerful tool, does not guarantee successful performance.

-Feedback that acts as **negative reinforcement** possesses unpleasant qualities that a participant will avoid in the future if possible. For feedback to act as negative reinforcement, its removal or avoidance must strengthen the action the participant needs to learn.

-Negative reinforcement is not the same as punishment. **Punishment** involves the instructor causing an unpleasant situation for the participant that occurs after the behaviour has taken place. It has the purpose of eliminating the unwanted behaviour. Negative reinforce ment involves removing an unpleasant situation that occurs because of the participant's performance. The unpleasant situation needs a change in behaviour to remove it. The participant is forced to improve to remove the unpleasant experience. Punishment should never be used by the instructor.

3.Motivation for skill learning

-This type of feedback provides knowledge that directs the participant's motivation. For example, a participant who is shown how to perform a particular exercise, then practices it and through intrinsic and extrinsic feedback they can gauge the distance between their present performance and their goal performance. This helps the participant to modify their behaviour, until through learning, their present performance and goal performance become identical.

-This type of feedback can also have an effect on how much energy the participant will expend on future tries at performing the technique. For example, if a participant receives intrinsic or extrinsic feedback indicating that the difference between their current perform ance and their goal performance has decreased, then they are likely to perceive that they are improving and that they are making progress. This type of feedback can be very satisfying for the participant and act as an incentive to continue to use their available energy to try to improve their present performance until the goal performance has been achieved.

-However, if this type of feedback indicates that there is no difference between their present performance and their goal performance, or even worse, that the difference has actually increased, then the participant will perceive that they have made no improvement or no progress has taken place. This can be very frustrating and may serve to reduce the amount of energy used for future attempts to learn or even to devote no energy to it whatsoever - the participant will not try very hard in the future or may just give up.

Shaping

•Shaping is basically the use of positive reinforcement so that the participant's performance is moulded closer and closer to the goal performance. The instructor positively reinforces closer and closer approximations of the correct technique.

•New participants learning a new technique are unlikely to perform it correctly on their first attempts. The instructor needs to reinforce any action that resembles the goal technique. After subsequent attempts, the fitness instructor should make the reinforcement more and more exact and only given when the participant's performance closely resembles the correct technique.

Skill modification

•To increase the chances of a correct performance taking place, the instructor needs to use extrinsic feedback in the following way:

 -Give extrinsic feedback that positively reinforces the correct skill performance;
 -Provide a model and give extrinsic feedback that reinforces the performance of the model.

•To decrease the chances of an incorrect performance taking place, the instructor needs to use extrinsic feedback in the following way:

 -Withdraw extrinsic feedback that acts as reinforcement;
 -Give extrinsic feedback that positively reinforces a participant for not making a mistake.

Using **"IDEA"** can help you teach the exercises or activities in the most efficient way possible:

I: Introduction
D: Demonstration
E: Explanation
A: Activity

A possible script for an exercise might be:

I: "This is the _____ exercise" or "This is called _____"
D: [Demonstrate the exercise or activity].
E: "Remember to …", "As you can see…", "Please observe …" [Give teaching points].
A: "Now let me see you try it." [talk the participants into position, reinforce the teaching points, observe, correct and provide feedback].

At all times try to keep the information brief and to the point.

PERSONAL QUALITIES OF THE TEACHER

Below are listed some simple guidelines that will help:

1.**Personality** - Try to be friendly and approachable so that participants are not afraid to talk to you. Be encouraging and enthusiastic to help motivate the participants - your enthusiasm may 'rub off' on them leading to a healthier lifestyle. Be understanding and professional at all times so that the participants learn to trust you. This list of personality traits is potentially endless, the important point to remember is that the relationship you form with your participants should be professional and based on mutual respect and trust;

2.**Appearance** - A smart, clean, professional appearance is essential at all times and you must always wear the appropriate clothing. Remember that you act as a role model for your participants - a scruffy and unkempt appearance may indicate to them a disorganised and muddled approach to teaching. In addition, you should not wear large items of jewellery and be careful of any body piercing. Also ensure footwear is safe and suitable for the training activities and environment and that they are not worn;

3.**Communication** - You must speak loud enough so all can hear. Your voice should vary in pitch and tone to make it interesting and convey the right atmosphere appropriate to the section of the class. Slow down your speech to an understandable speed and articulate your words. Instructions and teaching points should be concise. Body language, or non-verbal communication, is also extremely important;

4.Movement quality - You must have a good level of personal fitness and be able to demonstrate and perform all exercises to a high standard. You, as the teacher, act as a role model for the participants in your class, and any demonstrations you perform must be accurate so they learn the correct technique.

EVALUATING A CIRCUIT TRAINING SESSION

Evaluation is an essential component of the coaching process. This is because although a training session may look effective and enjoyable on your planning documents, in reality, the delivery of the training session may be very different. Evaluation is often neglected, and yet, by evaluating sessions the instructor is consistently monitoring their performance with the aim of improving. Evaluation can be done in three ways:

1.*Self evaluation*. Immediately after the session (not several hours or days later when your memory of the session is hazy!) reflect upon the following:

-What went well?
-Why did it go well?
-What went badly?
-Why did it go badly?
-Were the aims and objectives achieved?
-What action needs to be taken to progress further?
-What improvements can you make to your coaching?
-What changes or actions do you need to make for your next session?
-What did your participants enjoy or dislike?
-How did the participants behave and respond to you?
-Did you manage and organise the group effectively?

The above information is essential for planning future sessions and for assessing whether they are on target for reaching their and the programme's long term goals. Write down any action points that arise from your evaluation. Implement these action points into the planning and delivery of your next session.

2.*Participant evaluation*. By asking the participants for feedback on the session, it is possible to determine what they considered about the following:

-What they found enjoyable.
-How the session can be made more enjoyable.
-What they disliked and why.
-What they felt they had gained or benefited from the session.
-What they would like to see in future sessions.

It is advisable to write down this feedback as soon as possible so it is not forgotten. Add your own reflections and thoughts to this feedback and, if possible, try to implement some of these suggestions.

3.*Peer evaluation*. This involves another teacher or instructor observing you deliver a training session. This is an excellent way of gaining objective feedback regarding your teaching. It is likely they will see something in your teaching that you will never have considered otherwise, or they may give you an alternative perspective with helpful teaching tips. Ask other teachers or instructors you are comfortable with, and do not get offended if they pick up on many aspects of your teaching as they are only (hopefully) trying to help you. Once again, document the feedback and any action points taken.

101 Circuit Cards - Set A

The following pages are additional teaching points for use with circuit cards, sets A-C

A1	Abdominal Curl	Rectus abdominis Knees bent, feet flat on floor. Keep lower back pressed into floor throughout. Look directly at same spot on ceiling at all times, keeping neck aligned with spine. Only raise shoulders a few inches off the floor, sliding hands up thighs onto knees.
A2	Alternate Leg Raises	Rectus abdominis Do not attempt if student has bad back. Keeping lower back pressed into floor at all times, and arms supporting the body on either side, raise and lower alternate legs, keeping them straight, and off the floor at all times.
A3	Alternate Double Crunch	Rectus abdominis Do not attempt if student has bad back. Keeping lower back pressed into floor at all times, raise shoulders a few inches off floor, whilst pulling knees into chest. Return to starting position and repeat. Look directly at same spot on ceiling at all times, keeping neck aligned with spine.
A4	Abdominal Press	Rectus abdominis Keep body aligned in one straight line, with back straight, bottom down, & looking at floor, whilst supporting body on forearms & toes. Isometric exercise.
A5	Alternate Leg V-sits	Rectus abdominis Do not attempt if student has bad back. Keeping lower back pressed into floor at all times, raise one leg (keeping it straight), whilst raising shoulders off the floor a few inches. Lower and repeat with other leg. Look directly at same spot on ceiling at all times, keeping neck aligned with spine.
A6	Back Extensions	Erector spinae Keeping hips, knees & toes touching the floor at all times, raise the shoulders a few inches off the floor. Lower & repeat. Look at the floor throughout, keeping the neck in alignment with the back throughout.
A7	Calf Raises	Gastrocnemius, soleus Stand upright, with back straight & head up, looking forward. Make sure knees are not locked. Raise heels off floor, until the only point of contact with the floor is the ball of the foot. Lower & repeat.
A8	Close Leg Squats	Quadricep group, gluteus maximus, Hamstrings Stand with feet together, back straight & looking forward, keeping neck aligned with back. Bend knees up to 90' (less if student has bad knees), making sure knees don't come further forward than the toes. Straighten up again to starting position without locking knees straight.
A9	Crunches	Rectus abdominis Keeping lower back pressed into floor at all times, raise shoulders a few inches off the floor, bringing chest towards the raised knees. Lower & repeat. Look directly at same spot on ceiling at all times, keeping neck aligned with spine.
A10	Doggy Kicks	Gluteus minimus & medius, Tensor fasciae latae Kneel on all fours, looking at floor & keeping back straight throughout. Keeping leg bent, raise it up to the side to point of tension. Lower & repeat.
A11	Double Crunch	Rectus abdominis Do not attempt if student has a bad back. Keeping lower back pressed into the floor at all times, raise shoulders a few inches of the floor, whilst both legs (kept straight) are lifted towards the shoulders. Lower & repeat. Look directly at same spot on ceiling at all times, keeping neck aligned with spine.
A12	Extended Leg Crunches	Rectus abdominis Keeping lower back pressed into floor at all times, and legs raised throughout, raise shoulders a few inches off floor. Lower & repeat. Look directly at same spot on ceiling at all times, keeping neck aligned with spine.
A13	Extension Press Ups	Triceps, anterior deltoids, pectoralis major Looking at floor & keeping back straight throughout, raise & lower elbows to the floor. Keep hands extended in front of body, shoulder width apart at all times.
A14	Floor Dips	Triceps Keep back straight & head up at all times. Ensure knees are bent with feet flat on floor. Lower trunk to floor by bending arms, and then raise & repeat.
A15	Flutter Kicks	Rectus abdominis, iliopsoas, sartorius Keep back straight & head up throughout. Sit on bench, grasping lip for support. Lean backwards & raise both legs (keeping them straight) off floor. Raise & lower alternate legs at speed.
A16	Front Lying Leg Raises	Erector spinae, gluteus maximus, hamstring group Keep back straight & head facing floor throughout. The trunk and hips are in contact with the floor at all times. Raise one leg as high as possible, while the other remains on the floor. Lower, & repeat with other leg.
A17	Hanging Leg Raises	Rectus abdominis, iliopsoas, sartorius Using an overhand or underhand grip, grasp a chin up bar & hang, keeping back straight & looking forwards throughout the exercise. Keeping knees together, raise them to chest & then lower.
A18	Knee To Side Obliques	Internal & external obliques Lie on floor, knees bent & feet as close to the bottom as possible. Lower knees to one side, whilst keeping back flat on floor. Keeping lower back flat on floor, raise shoulders a few inches, whilst looking directly upwards, keeping the neck aligned with the spine. Lower & repeat.
A19	Kickbacks	Gluteus maximus, hamstring group Rest on all fours, & keep back straight & head facing floor at all times. Lift & pull one knee into chest, then extend it backwards & lift towards ceiling. Repeat procedure.
A20	Lizards	Erector spinae Lie face down with arms extended in front. Keeping hips & upper body pressed into floor throughout, raise left leg & right arm as high as possible. Lower & repeat on other side.
A21	Lunges	Quadriceps group Stand with feet shoulder width apart, toes facing forward. Keep back straight & head up at all times. Take a step forward with one leg, bending both knees. Make sure the knee of the front leg does not go past the toes, and the rear knee does not touch the floor. Push back to the starting position & repeat with the other leg.

A22	Lying Adductors	Adductor group & gracilis Lie on side with upper leg bent & foot flat on floor in front of lower leg. Keep neck aligned with straight back & use hands to support upper body. Raise lower leg & then lower.
A23	Lying Abductors	Gluteus minimus & medius, tensor fasciae latae Lie on side with lower leg bent for support. Keep neck aligned with straight back & use hands to support upper body. Raise upper leg as high as possible, & then lower.
A24	Lying Side Bends Oblique	Internal & external obliques Knees bent, feet flat on floor. Look directly at same spot on ceiling at all times, keeping neck aligned with spine. Rest head on one hand and reach forward with the other, trying to touch feet. Lower & repeat.
A25	Hanging Oblique Twists	Internal & external obliques, iliopsoas, sartorius Using an overhand or underhand grip, grasp a chin up bar & hang, keeping back straight & looking forwards throughout the exercise. Keeping knees together, raise them to one side, lower & repeat on the other side.
A26	Moving Squat	Quadricep group, Gluteus maximus, Hamstrings Stand with feet together, toes facing forward. Squat down, keeping back straight & looking forward, ensuring knees do not extend in front of toes. Rise, turning toes out. Squat & then rise lifting onto balls of feet & lowering balls of feet so toes facing forward. Repeat procedure until feet are shoulder width apart, then repeat moving feet inwards. Squat no more than 90'.
A27	Narrow Arm Press Ups	Triceps, anterior deltoids Get into push up position with hands touching underneath chest. Keeping back straight throughout and head facing the floor, lower body to floor by bending arms. Raise & repeat.
A28	Nasty Abs	Rectus abdominis Should not be attempted by any student with a bad back. Lie down, crossing one leg over the other. Keep lower back pressed into floor throughout. Look directly at same spot on ceiling at all times, keeping neck aligned with spine. Only raise shoulders a few inches off the floor, whilst raising legs to ceiling. Lower & repeat.
A29	Oblique Curl Ups	Internal & external obliques Lie with knees bent & feet flat on floor. Keep lower back pressed into floor throughout. Look directly at same spot on ceiling at all times, keeping neck aligned with spine. Place right hand on left thigh, raise right shoulder off floor a few inches, twisting trunk sliding right hand up to the left knee. Lower & repeat.
A30	One Arm Press Ups	Triceps, anterior deltoids, pectoralis major Not for the beginner! Get into press up position with legs spread wide. Place one arm behind back & the other directly under the chest. Lower body to floor by bending arm, then raise & repeat. Keep back straight throughout, whilst looking at floor, keeping the neck aligned.
A31	Prayer Curls	Rectus abdominis Knees bent, feet flat on floor. Keep lower back pressed into floor throughout. Look directly at same spot on ceiling at all times, keeping neck aligned with spine. Only raise shoulders a few inches off the floor, whilst pushing hands through the gap between the knees.
A32	Press Ups	Triceps, anterior deltoids, pectoralis major Get into push up position. Keep back straight, looking at floor throughout, and bottom down so body is completely straight. Lower body to floor by bending arms. Raise body & repeat.
A33	Press Up Bench Walks	Triceps, anterior deltoids, pectoralis major Get into push up position facing a bench. Keeping back straight & looking at floor throughout, use the hands to step up and down from the bench.
A34	Press Up Dips	Triceps, anterior deltoids, pectoralis major Get into push up position Keeping back straight & looking at floor throughout, lower body to floor by bending arms, & then slide body forwards. Raise body back to starting position & repeat.
A35	Pull Ups	Biceps, posterior deltoids, latissimus dorsi Hang from a chin up bar using an underhand grip, so feet are off the floor. Keep back straight & look forwards throughout. Raise the body, pulling chin to the bar by bending the arms. Lower & repeat.
A36	Punch Sit Ups	Rectus abdominis Lie on floor with legs bent, & feet flat on floor. Keep lower back pressed into floor throughout. Look directly at same spot on ceiling at all times, keeping neck aligned with spine. Raise shoulders off floor & double punch. Lower and repeat.
A37	Rear Leg Raised Lunge	Quadricep group Stand with one foot on a bench placed behind with toes facing forward. Keep back straight & head up at all times. Bend both knees, making sure the knee of the front leg does not go past the toes. Push back to the starting position & repeat with the other leg.
A38	Reverse Ab Curls	Rectus abdominis Do not attempt if student has bad back. Pull both knees into chest & push to ceiling (raising bottom off floor). Reverse the process & repeat. Keep upper back & head pressed into floor at all times.
A39	Reverse Abdominals	Rectus abdominis Do not attempt if student has bad back. Raise both legs so they are pointing to ceiling (keeping straight). Push legs up to ceiling raising bottom off floor. Lower & repeat. Keep upper back & head pressed into floor at all times.
A40	Scissor Kicks	Rectus abdominis Do not attempt if student has bad back. Lie on floor with legs raised throughout, place hands under bottom for support. Spread legs to side, & then back crossing over. Keep upper back & head pressed into floor at all times.
A41	Shoulder Squeezes	Trapezius, rhomboids Lie face down, arms 90' to side & bent. Whole body remains pressed into floor throughout, with head looking at floor. Raise elbows as high as possible. Lower & repeat.
A42	Side Lunges	Quadricep group Stand, feet shoulder width apart, toes facing forward. Keeping back straight & looking forward, step to side with one foot, bending that knee, & keeping the other straight. Push back & repeat. Bend knees no more than 90'.
A43	Side Step & Squat	Quadricep group, gluteus maximus Stand, feet shoulder width apart. Squat, making sure knees do not extend in front of toes and knees bend no more than 90'. Stand, slide left foot to right foot, slide right foot out to side. Repeat procedure. Back straight, head up throughout.

A44	Single Leg Curl	Hamstring group Rest on all fours. Keeping back straight & looking at floor, raise one leg, & then bend, bringing heel to bottom. Lower & repeat.
A45	Single Leg Squat	Quadricep group Stand on one leg (hold on if balance a problem). Keeping back straight & looking forward, Squat, ensuring knee does not extend in front of toes, & no more than 90'. Straighten up & repeat.
A46	Sit Ups	Rectus abdominis Do not attempt if student has bad back. Knees bent, feet flat on floor. Look directly at same spot on ceiling at all times, keeping neck aligned with spine. Raise trunk off the floor, sliding hands up thighs onto knees. Lower & repeat.
A47	Squat Calf Raises	Soleus Stand in a squat position, feet shoulder width apart, with knees bent at 90', back straight & head up. Raise heels off floor onto balls of feet. Lower & repeat.
A48	Squat Front Kicks	Quadricep group, gluteus maximus, sartorius, iliopsoas Stand, feet shoulder width apart. Squat, making sure knees do not extend in front of toes and knees bend no more than 90'. Stand, raising one knee to chest & then pushing forward at waist height. Return to starting position & repeat. Back straight & head up throughout.
A49	Squat Knee Raises	Quadricep group, gluteus maximus, sartorius, iliopsoas Stand, feet shoulder width apart. Squat, making sure knees do not extend in front of toes and knees bend no more than 90'. Stand, raising one knee to chest. Lower & repeat. Back straight & head up throughout.
A50	Squat Thrusts	Quadricep group, gluteus maximus, sartorius, iliopsoas Start in press up position. Keeping back straight & head up throughout, pull both knees into chest & thrust them back out. Repeat.
A51	Squats	Quadricep group, gluteus maximus Stand, feet shoulder width apart. Squat, making sure knees do not extend in front of toes and knees bend no more than 90'. Keep back straight & head up at all times. Stand & repeat.
A52	Standing Rear Squat	Quadricep group, gluteus maximus, hamstring group Stand, feet shoulder width apart. Squat, making sure knees do not extend in front of toes and knees bend no more than 90'. Keep back straight & head up at all times. Stand, & swing one leg to the rear. Lower & repeat.
A53	Standing Side Squat	Quadricep group, gluteus maximus, minimus & medius Stand, feet shoulder width apart. Squat, making sure knees do not extend in front of toes and knees bend no more than 90'. Keep back straight & head up at all times. Stand, & swing one leg up to the side. Lower & repeat.
A54	Static Abs	Rectus abdominis Do not attempt if student has bad back. Lie on floor, keeping back & head pressed into floor. Raise both legs off floor. Keeping them straight & together. Hold a few inches off the floor. Isometric exercise - must breath.
A55	Static Squats	Quadricep group, gluteus maximus Stand, feet shoulder width apart. Squat, making sure knees do not extend in front of toes and knees bend no more than 90'. Hold this position. Keep back straight & head up at all times
A56	Sumo Squats	Quadricep group, gluteus maximus, minimus & medius Stand, feet shoulder width apart. Squat, making sure knees do not extend in front of toes and knees bend no more than 90'. Keep back straight & head up at all times. Raise, lifting one knee to side. Lower & repeat.
A57	Toe Taps	Tibialis anterior Sit on bench, holding lip for support - feet out straight & resting on floor. Keeping back straight & head up, raise the toes of one foot towards the shin (keeping heel on floor). Lower & repeat with other foot. Repeat with speed
A58	Tricep Dips	Triceps, posterior deltoids Sit with hands on edge of bench either side of hips, with legs out straight resting on floor. Keeping back straight, head up & bottom as close to bench as possible. Lower bottom to floor by bending arms. Raise & repeat.
A59	V-sits	Rectus abdominis Do not attempt if student has bad back. Lie on floor, with arms outstretched behind head. Lift trunk and legs off floor (keeping both as straight as possible) bringing them together. Keep head aligned with spine. Lower & repeat.
A60	Wide Arm Press Ups	Pectoralis major, anterior deltoids, triceps Get into push up position, with hands double shoulder width apart. Keep back straight, looking at floor throughout, and bottom down so body is completely straight. Lower body to floor by bending arms. Raise body & repeat.
A61	Walking Lunges	Quadriceps Stand with feet shoulder width apart, toes facing forward. Keep back straight & head up at all times. Take a step forward with one leg, bending both knees. Make sure the knee of the front leg does not go past the toes, and the rear knee does not touch the floor. Bring trailing leg to the front & repeat the lunge moving forwards.
A62	Wall Squats	Quadricep group, gluteus maximus Stand, feet shoulder width apart, with back against wall. Squat, making sure knees do not extend in front of toes and knees bend no more than 90', keeping back pressed against wall, with head up.
A63	Wrist Rolls	Forearm flexors & extensors Sit with arms extended in front at shoulder height, holding a bar with an overhand grip in both hands. Keeping back straight & held up, roll the bar forwards by twisting the hands alternatively as fast as possible.
A64	Agility Run	Place cones forming the corners of a large square. Starting from one corner, run to the opposite corner, around the cone, & up to the corner on the same side of the square. Repeat, continue running in a figure of eight. Ensure the floor is not slippery, and free of debris.
A65	Butt Kicks	Jog on the spot, keeping back straight & head up. Place hands on bottom with palms facing out. Using alternate legs bring heels to palms. Repeat at a fast pace.
A66	Cossacks	Advanced exercise. Support body weight on hands & feet, with back to the ground. Keeping back straight throughout & looking at ceiling, lift & kick out alternate legs. Ensure knees are not locked when kicked.
A67	Leg Crossovers	Stand with feet double shoulder width apart, with back straight & looking forward throughout. Jump up, bringing legs in until one leg crosses in front of the other. Jump to starting position. Repeat so other leg crosses in front.
A68	Heel Taps	Jog on the spot, keeping back straight & head up, with arms hanging at sides. Using alternate legs bring heel to the palm of the opposite hand behind back (e.g. right heel to left hand). Repeat at a fast pace.
A69	High Knee Sprints	Jog on the spot, keeping back straight & looking forward. Raise alternate knees as high as possible, whilst swinging the arms. Repeat the exercise at a fast pace.

A70	Jumping Jacks	Start with feet together & hands by sides. Jump & land with feet double shoulder width apart & arms to the side at shoulder height. Jump, & land in starting position. Ensure back is kept straight with head up at all times.
A71	Jumpover	Stand to one side of bench, placing both hands on its lips. Keeping back straight & looking at bench at all times, perform a two-footed jump, clearing the bench & landing on the other side. Repeat at speed. Ensure both feet stay together throughout.
A72	Knee Raises	Stand with feet shoulder width apart & one leg in front of the other, arms out straight in front of shoulders. Lift the rear knee, thrusting forwards whilst bringing hands down to knee. Return & repeat at fast pace. Ensure back is kept straight with head up at all times.
A73	Lateral Step Ups	Standing side onto bench with feet shoulder width apart & toes facing forward. Lift up leg closest to bench placing foot onto it. Bring farthest leg up onto bench next to other foot. Step down with farthest leg, & then nearest leg. Repeat, ensuring whole of the foot is placed on bench, & back is straight with head up.
A74	Lateral Knee Raises	Stand with feet shoulder width apart & one leg forward. Keeping back straight & head up, lift rear knee to the side, bringing elbow down to meet the raising knee. Return to starting position & repeat.
A75	Crossovers	Stand with feet shoulder width apart, keeping back straight & head up. Raise right knee while bringing left elbow down so they meet. Repeat on other side.
A76	Shuttles	Run from one side of the training hall to the other (or from cone to cone). When one side has been reached, turn & run back to the other. Ensure the floor is not slippery & free from debris.
A77	Single Leg Squat Thrusts	Start in press up position, with one knee pulled into chest & the other out straight. Keeping back straight & head up throughout, swap leg positions by thrusting the pulled knee to a straight position, & pulling in the knee of the straight leg to chest. Repeat.
A78	Skipping	Stand upright, with back straight & head up, holding a skipping rope with both hands. Keeping hands by sides & by flicking the wrists, swing the rope over head, jumping over rope when it reaches the feet.
A79	Spotty Dogs	Stand with feet shoulder width apart, with right leg and left arm forward. Keeping back straight & head up, jump, changing positions of the arms & legs (so other leg & arm are now forward). Repeat at a fast pace.
A80	Spring Kicks	Stand with feet shoulder width apart, keeping back straight & head up throughout. Spring off one leg & kick out with the other at knee height, taking care not to lock out knee. Land & repeat with other leg, getting into a fast rhythm.
A81	Step Backs	Stand with feet shoulder width apart, keeping back straight & head up at all times. Step back with one leg onto the ball of the foot. Push back to the starting position, & repeat on alternate legs at a fast pace.
A82	Step Ups	Stand in front of a bench with feet hip width apart. Keeping back straight & head up throughout, step onto the bench with one foot, & then with the other. Ensure that the whole of the foot is on the bench, & toes are facing forwards at all times. Step down with the first leg, & then with the second. Keep in a fast rhythm for duration.
A83	Step Ups With Leg Raise	Stand in front of a bench with feet hip width apart. Keeping back straight & head up throughout, step onto the bench with one foot, & then lift body up by straightening the leg, whilst raising the rear knee as high as possible. Lower raised knee back down to floor, & then step down with the first foot. Ensure that the whole of the foot is on the bench, & toes are facing forwards at all times.
A84	Upright Windmills	Stand with feet shoulder width apart. Keeping back straight & head up, bend both knees slightly. Swing right arm to left knee, & then left arm to right knee. Repeat using a fast rhythm.
A85	Bench Press	Pectoralis major, triceps, anterior deltoid Lie face up on a bench holding dumbbells in each hand resting on chest, with the feet flat on floor either side of bench. Ensuring lower back & head is pressed into bench at all times, push dumbbells directly to ceiling above chest (without locking elbows & keeping wrists flat), & then lower back down to chest & repeat.
A86	Bent Over Rowing	Trapezius, rhomboid group, posterior deltoids, biceps. Stand with legs shoulder width apart, bending forward at the hips (keeping back straight & neck aligned with spine), with arms hanging down & a dumbbell in each hand. Lift dumbbells to shoulders, leading with the elbows. Lower & repeat.
A87	Bicep Curls	Biceps Stand with feet shoulder width apart, back straight & looking forward. Hold a dumbbell in each hand using an underhand grip. Keeping elbows pressed into the side of the body, raise the dumbbells to the shoulders. Lower & repeat. Avoid locking elbows and keep wrists flat.
A88	DB Bent Arm Pullover	Triceps Stand with feet shoulder width apart, keeping back straight & head up at all times. Hold a dumbbell in each hand, with arms raised up to ceiling & straight, with palms facing forward. Keeping elbows fixed in place bend elbows, lowering weight to the rear. Raise to starting position & repeat. Keep wrists flat throughout.
A89	DB Forward Raises	Pectoralis major Stand with feet shoulder width apart, back straight & head up throughout. Hold dumbbell in each hand at waist height, with palms facing the body. Keeping arms straight, lift alternate arms directly up to shoulder height. As one arm raises the other lowers. Keep wrists flat throughout.
A90	DB Lateral Raises	Lateral deltoids Stand with feet shoulder width apart, keeping back straight & head up at all times. Hold a dumbbell in each hand, holding to the side of thighs with palms facing inwards. Raise dumbbells out to the sides keeping arms straight. Keep wrists flat throughout, & stop when dumbbells get to shoulder height. Lower & repeat.
A91	DB Tricep Press	Triceps Stand with feet shoulder width apart, keeping back straight & head up at all times. Hold a dumbbell in one hand, with that arm raised up to ceiling & straight, palm facing forward. Keeping elbow fixed in place & supported by other hand, bend elbow, lowering weight to the rear. Raise & repeat. Keep wrist flat throughout.
A92	Floor Lateral Raises	Lateral deltoids Lie on floor with legs bent for support, keeping back straight & head up at all times. Hold a dumbbell in top hand. Raise dumbbell up to the side keeping arms straight. Keep wrists flat throughout, & stop when dumbbell gets to shoulder height, pointing to ceiling. Lower & repeat.
A93	Flyes	Pectoralis major, anterior deltoid Lie on bench, with lower back & head pressed into it, & feet flat on floor either side. Hold dumbbell in each hand, held with arms straight directly over chest (palms facing in). Keeping arms straight & wrists flat, lower to side as far as shoulder level. Raise & repeat.

A94	Hammer Curls	Biceps, forearm flexors & extensors Stand with feet shoulder width apart, back straight & look ahead. Hold dumbbell in each hand using underhand grip, with palms facing in. Keeping elbows pressed into side of body, raise dumbbells to shoulders, turning forearms until palms face ceiling. Lower, twisting other way, & repeat. Avoid locking elbows and keep wrists flat.
A95	Prone Flyes	Trapezius, rhomboids group Kneel with one knee raised/foot flat on floor. Keeping back straight & head aligned, lean trunk forward, until chest rests on raised knee. Hold dumbbell in each hand, palms facing in. Lift arms to side, leading the movement with elbows (arms slightly bent & wrists flat). Stop when dumbbells are shoulder height. Lower & repeat.
A96	Shoulder Press	Lateral deltoids, triceps Stand with feet shoulder width apart, keeping back straight & head up throughout. Hold the dumbbells at shoulder height, & push the weights directly up towards the ceiling (without locking elbows & keeping wrists flat). Lower & repeat.
A97	Shoulder Shrugs	Trapezius, rhomboids group Stand with feet shoulder width apart, back straight & looking forward. Hold a weight in each hand, with arms straight & resting on the outside of the thighs (where they remain throughout the exercise). Raise the shoulders as if shrugging, & then lower & repeat.
A98	Single Arm Row	Latissimus dorsi, biceps Place one knee & hand on bench. Other foot on floor & parallel with knee on bench. Keeping back straight & looking at bench, lift dumbbell up to armpit, keeping arm close to body & leading the movement with the elbow. Lower & repeat. Avoid locking elbow & keep wrist flat.
A99	Straight Arm Pullover	Pectoralis major, latissimus dorsi Lie on bench, pressing back & head into it, with feet flat on floor either side. Holding dumbbell in each hand lift so arms are straight & above chest. Lower behind head until slight stretch is felt. Pull dumbbells back to stomach in wide arc. Repeat.
A100	Tricep Kickbacks	Triceps Stand with feet shoulder width apart, back straight, head up, & holding a dumbbell in each hand. Bend elbows lifting dumbbells to ribs, so elbows are pointing backwards. Keep elbows fixed, & straighten arms. Bend arms & repeat.
A101	Upright Rows	Trapezius, biceps, anterior deltoids Stand with feet shoulder width apart, keep back straight & head up throughout. Hold dumbbell in each hand & keep weights close to the body - lead the movement with elbows, raising weights to chin. Lower & repeat.

101 Circuit Cards - Set B

B1	180° Depth Jump	Do not attempt if student has bad knees or back. After stepping off bench, land on both feet, bending at knees. Immediately straighten them in order to jump up and twist. Ensure both feet land on other bench. With beginners, only use one bench.
B2	360° Depth Jump	Do not attempt if student has bad knees or back. After stepping off bench, land on both feet, bending at knees. Immediately straighten them in order to jump up and twist.
B3	Alternate Split Squat Jump	Keeping back straight and head up at all times, jump from a lunge position straight up switching leg positions whilst in the air. When landing bend both knees ensuring rear knee doesn't touch the floor and front knee doesn't extend beyond toes.
B4	Alternate Push-off	Keeping back straight and head up throughout, always ensure that the whole of the foot is on the bench.
B5	Alternate Bounding	Keeping back straight and head up throughout, thrust rear knee as high as possible to the front, landing on that foot. Repeat using alternate legs. Use arm swing to help with distance and height. Bend knees on impact with floor.
B6	Alternate DB Punch	Stand with feet shoulder width apart, knees slightly bent with back straight and head up at all times. Holding a dumbbell in each hand at chest height, punch forward making sure elbows are not locked.
B7	Astride Jumps	Keeping back straight and head up at all times, drop both feet off bench, bending knees to absorb the impact. Immediately push-up landing back on the bench. Ensure both feet are completely on the bench.
B8	Advancing Side Kick	Place foot into partner's stomach keeping foot parallel to floor. Pivot on the support foot so toes face away from partner. Do not bend kicking leg or attempt to push partner back with it. Instead, push-off with the supporting leg pushing partner backwards.
B9	Bench Lateral Jumps	Stand with feet shoulder width apart side onto bench. Keeping back straight and head up at all times. Bend knees and then immediately jump up side ways over the bench. On landing, bend knees to absorb the impact and repeat the exercise.
B10	Bench Hops with Blitz	Stand facing row of benches, bend knees and immediately perform two-footed hops over each bench, making sure knees are bend on impact before explosively hopping over the next bench. After hopping the last bench, sprint forwards throwing left and right punches as fast as possible.
B11	Bench Hops with 180° Turn	Stand facing the bench with back straight and head up at all times. Bend knees and immediately jump up over bench. Whilst in the air, twist the body round so you land facing the opposite way. Bend knees on impact and repeat.
B12	Bench-to-Bench Jump	Stand with feet shoulder width apart facing a row of benches. Keeping back straight and head up at all times, bend knees and immediately perform a two-footed hop onto first bench (ensure whole of the foot is on bench). Then step off bench, bending knees upon contact with the floor. Repeat jumping onto and off the benches.
B13	Bum Jumps	Keeping back straight and head up at all times, drop both feet off bench, bending knees to absorb the impact, until the bottom touches the bench (make sure knees do not bend more than 90°). Immediately push-up landing back on the bench. Ensure both feet are completely on the bench.
B14	Beam Push Ups	Stand facing a beam which is at shoulder height. Place both hands onto beam. Bend knees and by using the power of the legs and the arms, push-up as high as possible. Bend knees when landing. Ensure back is kept straight and head kept in alignment throughout.
B15	Burpees	Not recommended for those with bad knees or bad backs. Back straight and head up throughout. Perform squat thrust, followed by a vertical jump.

B16	Corner Jumps	Keeping legs and back straight and with head up. Push upwards with feet, leaping over one side of the square with each jump.
B17	Crouching Leg Hop	Crouching down in front of bench. Leap up and over bench landing on the other side. Ensure back is kept straight at all times and when landing bend the knees to absorb the impact.
B18	Combination Bounding	Whilst jogging, hop from one foot to the other, adding bounds onto the other leg. Use arm swings to aid height and distance. Make sure knees are bent when landing to absorb the impact.
B19	Chest Slap Press Ups	Keeping back straight and looking at floor at all times. Lower body to the floor, push explosively so that upper body and arms are pushed clear of the floor. Clap hands to chest before putting them back into press up position.
B20	Clap Press Ups	Keeping back straight and looking at floor at all times. Lower body to the floor, push explosively so that upper body and arms are pushed clear of the floor. Clap hands together before putting them back into press up position.
B21	Double Ankle Hop	Stand with feet shoulder width apart, back straight and head up at all times. Keeping legs straight, leap straight into the air only using the ankles.
B22	Double Lateral Ankle Hop	Stand with feet shoulder width apart, back straight and head up at all times. Keeping legs straight, leap from side to side, only using the ankles.
B23	Double Lateral Jumps	Stand with feet shoulder width apart, keeping back straight and head up. Swing right arm and leg in front of left arm and leg. Then jump to the right as far as possible, landing on both feet.
B24	Diagonal Bench Jumps	Stand at the end of the bench with back straight and head up with feet together. Bend both knees, then immediately jump diagonally forwards to the other side of the bench. Bend knees on landing and repeat.
B25	Double Leg Hops	Stand with feet shoulder width apart. Keeping back straight and head up, bend both knees and immediately jump forward as far as possible. Bend knees on landing and repeat.
B26	Depth Jump	Stand on bench with feet shoulder width apart. Keeping back straight and head up at all times, step off the bench and on landing bend the knees, immediately jumping as high as possible.
B27	Depth Jump to Bench	Stand on bench with feet shoulder width apart. Keeping back straight and head up at all times, step off the bench and on landing bend the knees, immediately jumping onto the next bench.
B28	Depth Jump to Jumping Kick	Stand on bench with feet shoulder width apart. Keeping back straight and head up at all times, step off the bench and on landing bend the knees, immediately perform a jumping kick of your choice.
B29	Depth Jump to Bag Blitz	Stand on bench with feet shoulder width apart. Keeping back straight and head up at all times, step off the bench and on landing bend the knees, immediately charge at punch bag, punching hard and fast.
B30	Depth Jump over Bench	Stand on bench with feet shoulder width apart. Keeping back straight and head up at all times, step off the bench and on landing bend the knees, immediately jump over second bench.
B31	Depth Jump to Standing Long Jump	Stand on bench with feet shoulder width apart. Keeping back straight and head up at all times, step off the bench and on landing bend the knees, immediately jump as far forward as possible.
B32	DB Alternate Arm Swing	Stand with feet shoulder width apart, knees slightly bent with back straight and head up at all times. Holding a dumbbell in each hand, and keeping arms slightly bent, swing forwards and upwards with one arm, whilst the other swings back.
B33	DB Horizontal Swing	Stand with feet shoulder width apart, knees slightly bent with back straight and head up at all times. Holding one dumbbell in both hands at chest height, swing the dumbbell from side to side.
B34	DB Vertical Swing	Stand with feet shoulder width apart, knees slightly bent with back straight and head up at all times. Holding one dumbbell in both hands at chest height, swing the dumbbell upwards and downwards.
B35	Front Bench Hops	Stand facing a row of benches with feet together and back straight. Keeping feet together jump over each bench remembering to bend knees when landing.
B36	Front Bench Jump	Stand with feet shoulder width apart and hands behind head, facing the bench. Bend the knees, immediately jumping onto the bench. Step down off bench, bending the knees and repeating. Make sure the whole of the foot lands on the bench at all times.
B37	Hip Twist Ankle Hop	Stand with feet shoulder width apart and back straight with head up. Without bending the knees, only the ankles, hop up twisting the hips. Land and repeat twisting back and forth.
B38	Heel Flick Tuck Jump	Stand with feet shoulder width apart. Back straight and looking forwards throughout. Bend knees and immediately jump straight up. Whilst in the air touch heels to bottom. Use arm swing to aid height.
B39	High Knee Skipping	Stand with one leg in front of the other, feet shoulder width apart. Lift the rear knee to the front whilst pushing off with the other. Upon landing, repeat with the other leg. Use arm swing to increase height and distance.
B40	Lateral Bench Shuffle	Stand side on to bench with nearest foot on top of bench. Push upwards with leg, jumping over to the other side of the bench. Land with the other foot on top of the bench and repeat. Make sure the whole of the foot is on bench.
B41	Lateral Bench Hops	Stand side on to bench with feet shoulder width apart. Bend knees and jump sideways over bench, landing on outside foot only (inside is raised and off floor or bench). Push off outside foot to jump back over the bench, again landing on the outside foot.
B42	Lateral Step Ups	Stand side on to bench with the nearest foot on top. Straighten the leg on bench, raising the body. Then bend knee lowering to starting position. Repeat.
B43	Lateral Bench Jump	Stand side onto bench with feet shoulder width apart. Bend knees, immediately jump onto the bench and then drop onto the other side. Bend knees on landing and repeat.
B44	Multiple Bench Squat Jumps	Stand in front of a row of benches with feet shoulder width apart and knees bent at right angles. Place hands behind head. Jump onto first bench landing in a squat position. Step to floor on the other side, bending knees and immediately jumping to the next bench. Repeat.
B45	Multiple Bench Single Squat Jumps	Stand on one leg in front of a row of benches with knee bent at right angle. Place hands behind head. Jump onto first bench landing in a single leg squat position. Hop to floor on the other side, bending knee and immediately jumping to the next bench. Repeat.
B46	Moving Split Jumps	Stand in a lunge position, with both knees bent at right angles. Keeping back straight and head up, push upwards and forwards into the air. Switch leg positions whilst in the air, and land, bending knees until a lunge position is reached (with other leg forward).
B47	Power Skipping	Stand with one leg in front of the other, feet shoulder width apart. Hold arms out in front of chest, and keeping back straight and head up, thrust rear knee upwards and forwards to chest, whilst attempting to touch foot with hands and hopping on other foot. Land and repeat with other leg.

B48	Retreating Side Kick	Place foot into partner's stomach keeping foot parallel to floor. Pivot on the support foot so toes face away from partner. Do not bend kicking leg. Instead, try to pull partner forwards by hopping backwards on the supporting leg.
B49	Resisted Running	Stand in front of partner with a rope/belt around your stomach (ends held by partner). Attempt to sprint forwards, lifting knees high and swinging arms. Partner offers resistance.
B50	Single Lateral Jump	Stand with feet shoulder width, back straight and head up. Bend knees and jump to the side. Land on the outside foot, bending it and then immediately pushing back in the opposite direction. Land on the other foot, bend and repeat.
B51	Squat Tuck Jumps	Stand with feet shoulder width apart, keeping back straight and head up throughout. Bend knees until hands touch floor immediately jump into air, pulling both knees into chest. On landing, bend knees to absorb the impact.
B52	Squat Jumps	Stand with feet shoulder width apart, keeping back straight and head up throughout. Bend knees until hands can touch the floor and then immediately jump vertically into the air keeping legs straight. On landing, bend knees to absorb the impact.
B53	Ski Jumps	Stand with feet shoulder width apart, keeping back straight and head up throughout. Bend knees and then jump up, twisting the whole body 180°. On landing, bend knees to absorb the impact, and then immediately spring up and repeat twisting the other way.
B54	Sergeant Jumps	Stand with feet shoulder width apart, keeping back straight and head up directly underneath an object. Bend knees and immediately spring upwards reaching for the object. On landing, bend knees to absorb the impact.
B55	Single Leg Bounds	Stand on one foot. Hop from this foot to the other as far forward as possible, bending knee on landing and then bounding once again. Use arm swings to help with distance.
B56	Side Skipping	Stand with feet together. With the outside foot, step to that side, swing the other foot along side the outside foot, so it pushes it to the side. Repeat. Movement should be dynamic, try to swing the feet as fast as possible.
B57	Single Leg Hops	Stand on one foot. Hop from this foot as far forward as possible, bending knee on landing and then hopping once again. Use arm swings to help with distance.
B58	Single Leg Push Off	Stand with one foot on the bench and one on the floor. Straighten the knee of the raised leg, pushing off and trying to gain as much height as possible. Land in the starting position and repeat (same leg pushes throughout).
B59	Squat Depth Jump	Stand in a squat position on bench. Knees bent at 90°, back straight and head up. Step off the bench, land bending knees and immediately jump forwards onto another bench. On landing bend knees to a squat position and repeat.
B60	Single Leg Depth Jump	Stand on bench with feet shoulder width apart. Keeping back straight and head up at all times, step off landing on one foot, bend the knee and immediately jump as far forward as possible landing on the same foot.
B61	Single Lateral Ankle Hop	Stand on one foot with the outside foot next to a bench. Bend knee and hop to the side, landing on the other foot next to the second bench. Bend knee and repeat jumping side to side, keeping back straight and head up throughout.
B62	Split Pike Jump	Stand with feet shoulder width apart back straight and head up. This exercise should not be attempted by beginning students, or those with bad knees or backs. Bend knees and jump up lifting both legs to the front of the body. Attempt to touch toes and land bending the knees to reduce the impact.
B63	Standing Long Jump	Stand with feet shoulder width apart, back straight and head up. Bend knees and immediately explode forwards as far as possible. Bend knees on landing. Use arm swing to aid jump.
B64	Split Squat Jump	Keeping back straight and head up at all times, jump from a lunge position straight up as high as possible. Land in same position, bend both knees ensuring rear knee doesn't touch the floor and front knee doesn't extend beyond toes.
B65	Standing Jump over Bench	Stand with feet shoulder width apart facing bench. Keeping back straight and head up, jump over the bench. Land, bending both knees. Turn and repeat.
B66	Standing Jump with Blitz	Stand with feet shoulder width apart facing bench. Keeping back straight and head up, jump over the bench. Land, bending both knees and immediately sprint forwards while punching with left and right hands. Use arm swing to help with the jump over the bench.
B67	Standing Jump with Bench Hop	Stand with feet shoulder width apart facing bench. Keeping back straight and head up, perform a standing long jump landing just in front of the bench. Upon landing bend both knees and immediately jump over the bench. Use arm swing to help with the jumps.
B68	Step Hops	Stand with feet shoulder width apart, back straight and head up at the bottom of steps/stairs. Place hands behind head, bend knees and jump to the first step. Bend knees on landing and jump to the next step. Repeat.
B69	Tuck Burpees	Not recommended for those with bad knees or bad backs. Back straight and head up throughout. Perform squat thrust, followed by a tuck jump.
B70	Tuck Jumps	Stand with feet shoulder width apart, back straight and head up. Bend knees and immediately jump vertically pulling both knees into chest. Bend knees on landing to reduce impact.
B71	Zig Zag Hop	Stand on one foot with the outside foot on the line. Bend knee and hop diagonally forwards and to the side, landing on the other foot on the other line. Bend knee and repeat jumping diagonally forward and from side to side, keeping back straight and head up throughout.
B72	MB Back Swing	Stand with feet shoulder width apart, holding a medicine ball with both hands, above & behind head (like a throw-in in football). Swing the ball forward & down, bending at the waist, throwing the ball behind you & through the legs.
B73	MB Back Toss	Stand with feet shoulder width apart, holding a medicine ball with both hands behind your back. The ball should be held with hands underneath & palms facing away from the body. Throw the ball forwards over the head, by pushing the arms backwards and bending at the waist.
B74	MB Forward Swing	Stand with feet shoulder width apart, holding a medicine ball with both hands. Bend forwards at the waist and knees, with the ball held between & behind the legs. Stand up quickly swinging the ball forwards, throwing it as high and far forward as possible.
B75	MB Heel Swing	Lie face down on the floor with a medicine ball held between the feet. Keeping knees pressed into the ground, back straight & head facing the ground, swing the lower legs upwards towards your bottom, throwing the ball upwards and forwards. To increase safety, have a partner ready to catch the ball.
B76	MB Leg Press	Lie on the floor with knees pulled into the chest, legs bent. Have a partner place a medicine ball onto your feet. Keeping your back & head pressed into the floor at al times. Push the pull upwards & forwards by straightening the legs as quickly as possible. Ensure that the knees are not locked at any time.
B77	MB Leg Toss	Hold on to a beam or chin up bar so that you are hanging clear of the floor. Your partner places a medicine ball between your feet. Keeping your back straight, swing your legs forwards & upwards releasing the ball so that it is thrown forwards.
B78	MB Lying Throw	Lie on the floor with knees bent and feet flat on floor. Arms are outstretched behind the head, holding a medicine ball in both hands. Sit up, swinging the arms forwards and upwards, throwing the ball as high & far as possible.
B79	MB Press	Stand with feet shoulder width apart, one leg in front of the other. Holding a medicine ball with both hands to the chest, push the ball forwards as hard & far as possible. Do not lock out the elbows when throwing.

B80	MB Throw	Kneel on the floor, holding a medicine ball in both hands, above & behind the head (just like a throw-in in football). Swing the ball forwards over your head, throwing the ball as high & far as possible.
B81	MB Toss	Stand with feet shoulder width apart, holding a medicine ball with both hands. Squat down, by bending at the knees & hips, & hold the ball between the legs, keeping the arms straight. Stand up quickly, swinging the arms forwards & upwards, flinging the ball as high & far as possible.
B82	MB Toss Overhead	Stand with feet shoulder width apart, holding a medicine ball with both hands. Bend forwards at the waist and knees, with the ball held between & behind the legs. Stand up quickly swinging the ball upwards & over the head, throwing it as high and far backward as possible.
B83	MB Twist Obliques	Lie on floor with knees bent & feet flat on floor. Keeping lower back pressed into the floor & head looking straight up, lift the right shoulder a few inches off the floor, whilst moving the ball to the left. Lower & repeat, this time lifting the left shoulder & moving the ball to the right.
B84	MB Twist-Toss	Stand with feet shoulder width apart, holding a medicine ball with both hands. Your partner stands behind you, with your backs touching. Holding the ball at waist height, twist your upper body to the right, passing the ball to your partner (who takes it). Immediately twist to the left to take the ball back off your partner. Repeat on both sides.
B85	Cradle Carry	Bend your knees, keeping back straight & head up, lift your partner so they rest across your shoulders. Make sure that feet are shoulder width apart. Perform a half squat, by bending the knees, ensuring that knees do not extend beyond toes, then straighten them. The heavier the partner, the harder the exercise. The deeper the squat, the harder the exercise.
B86	Donkey Raises	Stand facing a bench with body bent forward at 90°, so that hands are resting on the bench and the back is straight & parallel to the floor. A partner sits on your back, keeping as still as possible. Keeping the balls of the feet on the floor, raise the heels & then lower. The heavier the partner, the harder the exercise.
B87	Fireman's Carry	Bend your knees, keeping back straight & head up, lift your partner onto your shoulder. Make sure that feet are shoulder width apart. Perform a half squat, by bending the knees, ensuring that knees do not extend beyond toes, then straighten them. The heavier the partner, the harder the exercise. The deeper the squat, the harder the exercise.
B88	Partner Combined Press Up	Get into press up position, back straight, facing floor. Your partner gets into press up position with their feet resting on your back. You perform a press up, pause while your partner performs a press up, and partner pauses while you perform.
B89	Partner Curl Up	You and your partner sit on the floor facing each other. Interlock feet and bend knees. Lower backs to the floor, raise touching right hands to partner's shoulder. Lower & repeat using left hand.
B90	Partner Leg Curl	Lie face down on the floor with legs straight, & one crossed over the other. Your partner kneels to one side by your legs, and leans on your heels (adding resistance). Keeping knees pressed into floor, attempt to lift feet off floor bringing heels to bottom. Lower & repeat.
B91	Partner Leg Press	Lie on back with legs raised & held out straight. Partner holds onto your feet, pressing their weight onto your legs. Bend your knees & hips, pulling your knees into your chest. Push legs straight against your partner's resistance.
B92	Partner Pull Up	Lie on floor, holding arms straight up. Your partner stands over you, with one leg either side of your ribs, grabbing hold of your hands. Keeping your back straight, bend your arms, pulling yourself up towards your partner, stopping when your body touches your partner's legs. Lower & repeat.
B93	Partner Press Up	Get into press up position facing your partner, who is also in the same position. Lower body to the floor, and then raise up. After raising, you & partner clap right hands together. Return hand to floor & then repeat process, this time using the left hand. Ensure that the back is kept straight throughout & head faces the floor at all times.
B94	Partner Sergeant Jumps	Stand facing your partner at least a metre apart. Both simultaneously bend knees & immediately jump up as high as possible, swinging the arms to gain extra height. At the peak of the jump, you & your partner clap both hands against the others. Land & repeat.
B95	Partner Stand Ups	Make sure that you & your partner are similar in both height and weight. Sit on the floor, with your back touching the back of your partner. Both have legs out straight. Working as a team, both pull legs in so knees are bent & feet are flat on floor. Both need to push their backs against the others, whilst straightening the legs, in order to stand up. Bend knees to sit down again, & extend legs so they are straight. Repeat the process.
B96	Piggy Back Partner Squats	Stand with feet shoulder width apart, with your partner sitting on your back in 'piggy back' position. Keeping back straight & head up throughout, perform half squats by bending & straightening the knees & hips. The heavier the partner, the harder the exercise. The deeper the squat, the harder the exercise.
B97	Piggy Back Run	Stand with feet shoulder width apart, with your partner sitting on your back in 'piggy back' position. Keeping back straight & head up throughout, carry out shuttle runs from one side of the hall to the other. The heavier the partner, the harder the exercise. The faster you run, the harder the exercise.
B98	Side Kick Press	Stand side-on to a wall, with back straight & knee raised high with foot parallel to the floor. Place the sole of your foot into the stomach of your partner, who holds it in place. Whilst your partner offers some resistance, push to straighten your leg. Then bend the knee, returning to the start position. The more resistance the partner offers, the harder the exercise. Do not lock your knees when pushing out.
B99	Wheelbarrow Walking	Get into press up position with your partner standing between your legs. Your partner picks up your legs, & slowly walks forward, forcing you to walk on your hands, by placing one in front of the other. Ensure that the back is kept straight throughout, and you face the floor at all times. The faster the partner walks, the harder the exercise.
B100	Around the World	Stand with feet shoulder width apart, back straight and head up. Hold a dumbbell in each hand, hanging down by your sides. Keeping arms straight throughout, lift the weights to the front until the arms are pointing to the ceiling. Then, in a continuous motion, lower the weights to the side. Repeat.
B101	Breast Stroke	Stand with feet shoulder width apart, back straight and head up. Hold a dumbbell in each hand (with palms facing down), so they touch the chest at the start of the exercise. Press the weights forward, keeping arms parallel to the floor. When arms are fully extended (but not locked), pull the weights out to the side (keeping arms straight & at shoulder height). When the arms are either side of the body, bend the elbows and bring the weights back to the starting position.

BISHOP BURTON COLLEGE

101 Circuit Cards - Set C

C1	Push-up Match	Ensure body is kept straight throughout - and bottom doesn't lift up. Both can move around. Only wrists and forearms can be grabbed.
C2	Neck-pull in Push-up Position	Keep body straight throughout, with bottom down. Try and keep neck in line with spine. Do not let go of partner's neck during game. Can both move around. People with back problems should avoid this game.
C3	Circle Tag	Must stay in push-up position throughout, keeping both feet within the circle, and back straight. Tagger may move clockwise or anti-clockwise, partner must escape.
C4	Side Push-up Tag	Players must stay in side push-up position throughout, with supporting arm straight and never leaving the circle.. People with bad backs should avoid this game.
C5	Foot Tag	Ensure that all players keep contact very light, and are told to avoid hitting sensitive areas like the knees and ankles. It is a game, which should be fun, not painful.
C6	Shoulder Tag	Ensure that all players keep contact very light, and only tag the shoulders - no slapping the face, body or arms. It is a game, which should be fun, not painful.
C7	Thigh Tag	Ensure that all players keep contact very light, and only tag the outside of the thighs - no slapping the inside thigh or groin areas. It is a game, which should be fun, not painful.
C8	Reaction Tag	Only move to this game when the above three have been well practiced, and players can be trusted to play with control. Again, permit only light contact and specified targets.
C9	Single-leg Drill	Play game on mats for safety. Ensure both players know how to breakfall, in case one of them falls. No strikes permitted, only grabbing of the leg. Variation: combine with Reaction Tag.
C10	Sock Grab	Make sure that the sock/s can be easily retrieved by the partner. No striking allowed during the game. If playing the game kneeling, use a mat & players are not allowed to stand up at anytime. Variation: players play Reaction Tag & Sock Grab at same time.
C11	Balance Slap	Use a mat and wear gloves for added safety. Ensure hands, once hit, will not hit player in face. The player hitting must hit the hands with a straight arm.
C12	Slap Drill	Ensure that the hitter's attacks are light and controlled, aimed at the side of the blocker's head, not the face. Make sure that after each attack, arms are returned to the thighs.
C13	Kick-4-kick	Ensure both players take it in turns to kick. Make sure that beginner players do not make contact with their kicks, but are ready to evade or block just in case. Variation: 2 or 3 kick-4-kick combinations, or hand-&-foot combinations (alternate).
C14	Throw-4-throw	Use mats for safety. No striking allowed, only sweeps, trips, takedowns or throws. As soon as one player is thrown, he/she immediately stands up and performs a technique of their own.
C15	Cumulative Kicking Drill	Ensure that when the kicks are thrown, they do not connect with the other player - stand far apart. Do not try to block the other player's kicks.
C16	Boundary Fight	Mats can be used for added safety. Can be performed standing or kneeling, but in either case, the grip must not be broken at any time. Try to keep back straight & head up at all times.
C17	Cockfight	Use mats and wear safety equipment for added safety. Keep back straight and head up to avoid knocking heads during the game. Ensure that excessive contact is not permitted.
C18	Square Fight	Ensure mats are used for added safety. Players must maintain a grip throughout, & can only push or pull - no throws or striking permitted.
C19	Bar Entry Drill	No strikes or throws/takedowns allowed. A grip does not have to be maintained & pushing is allowed (but not to the head). Try to keep back straight & head up to avoid clashing heads.
C20	Neck Pulling Drill	Try to keep back straight & head up throughout. People with bad backs should avoid this one. No striking or throws/takedowns permitted - only pushing, pulling and turning.
C21	Leg Lock Fight Drill	Use mats for added safety. Keep legs locked together and maintain a grip throughout. Pushing & pulling is allowed, but no striking.
C22	Sumo	Use mats for added safety. Maintain grip throughout game, & only pulling, pushing & turning are permitted - no strikes, throws or takedowns.
C23	Sweep Contest	Use mats for safety. Ensure that both players have hands behind their backs throughout. Tell all players to keep contact very light, & to avoid making contact to knees & ankles.
C24	Footlifting Drill	Use mats for added safety. Keep a firm grip on partner's leg and neck throughout. No strikes or throws permitted, only pushing, pulling, lifting or turning.
C25	Tug-of-war Drill	Keep a firm grip throughout the game. No strikes or throws/takedowns allowed, only pulling of the partner's arm.
C26	Upper Body Wrestling	Keep a grip on each other throughout the game. No striking is permitted - only pushing, pulling, lifting & turning. Use mats for added safety.
C27	Footsweep Drill	Use mats for safety. No striking permitted, & lower legs must remain in contact throughout game. Try to keep back straight & head up at all times.
C28	Race to Opponent's Line	Use mats for added safety. No striking or throwing is permitted at any time, only pushing, lifting & carrying. Make sure that the level of contact is kept light.
C29	Path Race	Use mats for added safety. No striking, throwing, pushing or lifting allowed. Keep contact to a minimum throughout.
C30	Road Block	Specify which target area has to be tagged, e.g. shoulder. No other body part may be struck during the game & keep contact down to a minimum. No grappling is allowed.
C31	Hand Grab Drill	The catcher must keep his/her hands open & touching the chest at all times. The hitter should use control when hitting, and make little, if any, contact. The catcher shouldn't move his/her hands until they see the hitter punch.
C32	Foot Grab Drill	The catcher must keep his/her hands open & touching the waist/hips at all times. The hitter should use control when hitting, and make little, if any, contact. The catcher shouldn't move his/her hands until they see the hitter kick.
C33	Shadow Boxing	Keeping a good fighting stance throughout, practice good punching technique, footwork and evasion skills. Concentrate on good technique, & stringing combinations together.

C34	Shadow Kicking	Keeping a good fighting stance throughout, practice good kicking technique, footwork and evasion skills. Concentrate on good technique, & stringing combinations together.
C35	Shadow Sparring	A combination of the above 2 drills. Keeping a good fighting stance throughout, practice good punching & kicking technique, footwork and evasion skills. Concentrate on good technique, & stringing combinations together.
C36	Partner Shadow Sparring	Make sure contact is not allowed. This drill enables students to experience sparring without any apprehension or pain! Ensure they are far apart, but ready to block or evade if necessary.
C37	Focus Mitt Work	Hold straight for jab/cross. Face pads inwards for hooks. Face down for uppercuts. Pads can be held at face/body level. Focus mitt holder can attack with swings, forcing puncher to block/evade. Hand wraps/bag gloves can be worn.
C38	Thai Shield Work	Hold shields straight on for front/side kicks, jabs/crosses. Hold shields to the side to allow round kicks/hook punches. Face down for knee attacks/uppercuts. Hand wraps/bag gloves may be worn.
C39	Kick Shield	Hold shield straight on for front/side kicks. Hold shield to the side to allow round kicks/hook kicks.
C40	One Leg Sparring Drill	Mats & safety equipment can be used for additional safety. Ensure that contact is kept to a minimum & the raised leg does not touch the floor at any time.
C41	One-leg Boxing	Mats & safety equipment can be used for additional safety. Ensure that contact is kept to a minimum & the raised leg does not touch the floor at any time.
C42	One-leg Kicking	Kicker must remain on one leg at all times, kicking with the raised leg. Contact must be kept to a minimum. The defender should not block or parry the kicks too hard so the kicker loses balance. Use safety equipment & mats for safety.
C43	Hand-grab Tag	Contact must be kept to a minimum, and only on the specified target, e.g. shoulder. Once the tagger has had his hand or arm caught by one or both hands, it should be released and the game repeated.
C44	Crouch Fight	People with bad knees should not attempt this game. No striking or grappling is permitted, only pushing (keep the contact light). Mats should be used to aid safety.
C45	Side Push-up Fight	Stay in side push-up position at all times, with supporting arm straight. No striking or grappling is permitted, but each player may push the other off balance (no pushes to the head).
C46	Ball Wrestle	No striking or grappling should take place during this game. Both hands should remain on the ball at all times. Mats can be used to enhance safety.
C47	Bag Work	Concentrate on correct technique for both punches & kicks. Try to get the students to string combinations of punches & kicks together. Hand wraps/bag gloves may be worn.
C48	Floor to Ceiling Ball Work	Hand wraps/bag gloves may be worn to protect the hands. Students should concentrate on correct technique, and using combinations of punches, whilst evading the ball.
C49	Speed Ball Work	Hand wraps/bag gloves may be worn. Students should concentrate on correct technique, and using combinations of punches.
C50	Tag Sparring	Contact should be kept to a minimum throughout. Kicks should be above the waist, and open hand strikes should not be made to the face.
C51	Tag Boxing	Contact should be kept to a minimum throughout and open hand strikes should not be made to the face.
C52	FB Squats	Stand with feet shoulder width apart, loosen off knees. Place the ball so it is pressed against the lower back. Keep back straight and pressed against the ball at all times, bend knees until thighs are parallel to floor, making sure knees do not go in front of toes, then stand up by straightening legs - don not lock knees. Ball will roll up and down the back.
C53	FB Leg Curls	Lie face up on floor with feet resting on far side of ball and hands at side for support, with palms facing down. Lift hips off floor and bend knees bringing your heels to your bottom, rolling the ball close. Straighten legs - don't lock knees - and repeat for duration. Keep head resting on floor throughout.
C54	FB Hip Extensions	Lie face up on floor with feet resting on centre of ball and arms at side for support, palms facing down. Thrust hips upwards and then lower to floor. Repeat for duration. Keep head resting on floor throughout.
C55	FB Bridge Hip Extensions	Lie face up, with ball under upper back and feet flat on floor at all times. Keeping head supported and in line with spine, thrust hips towards ceiling and then lower to starting position. Repeat for duration.
C56	FB Oblique Curls	Lie face up with middle back resting on ball, knees bent, feet flat on floor throughout. Place hands by head. Raise right shoulder, twisting trunk to the left knee. Lower and repeat on other side.
C57	FB Opposites	Lie face down on ball, with arms extended in front, and feet behind, resting on the floor. Stomach should be resting on ball. Raise right leg and left arm off floor. Lower and repeat using the opposite limbs. Keep neck in alignment with spine throughout (i.e. look at floor).
C58	FB Trunk Curls	Lie face up with middle back resting on ball, knees bent with feet flat on floor, and hands by head. Keeping lower back on ball and feet on floor, raise shoulders and then return. Fix gaze at one point on ceiling above head, and keep looking at same spot throughout.
C59	FB Back Extensions	Lie face down with stomach on ball, with hands touching ears. Keeping toes touching floor and hips pressed against ball throughout, raise trunk and then lower. Keep neck in alignment with spine throughout (i.e. look at floor).
C60	FB Trunk Lateral Flexion	Lie on ball on your side. Place your top leg across your bottom leg for support. With hands touching head, bend the trunk sideways so it raises to the ceiling. Lower and repeat for duration. Repeat for other side. The trunk moves - not the head.
C61	FB Press Ups	Hands on floor, shoulder width apart, with feet resting on ball. Keeping the back straight and head in alignment with the spine, lower body to floor by bending arms. Straighten arms to raise. Repeat. Do not lock elbows.
C63	FB Shoulder Press	Sit on edge of ball with dumbbell in each hand at shoulder height. Without locking elbows, push dumbbells straight up to ceiling, and then lower to starting position. Repeat for duration. Back straight, head up.
C64	FB Lateral Raises	Sit on edge of ball with dumbbell in each hand hanging at side of body. Lift arms out to side until hands are at shoulder height. Lower arms back to side. Repeat for duration. Back straight, head up.
C65	FB Rotator Cuffs	Lie on ball on your side. Place your top leg across your bottom leg and lower arm to the floor for support. Hold a weight in the top hand. Bend top arm to right angles and fix elbow into ribs throughout. Lower weight by rotating arm towards stomach, and then raise by rotating towards ceiling. Try to keep head in alignment with spine throughout.
C66	FB Flyes	Lie face up with middle back on ball, dumbbell in each hand and hold so arms are straight and pointing to ceiling. Loose off arms and lower to sides so arms are outstretched. Return to starting position and repeat. Keep head in alignment with spine.

C67	FB Reverse Flyes	Lie face down, with stomach and lower chest supported by ball. Feet remain firmly on floor throughout. Hold a weight in each hand with arms hanging to floor (slightly bent). Raise elbows towards ceiling. Lower and repeat. Keep head in alignment with spine.
C68	FB Bench Press	Lie face up with middle back on ball, holding a dumbbell in each hand on the chest. Push each dumbbell upwards towards ceiling and then return to chest. Repeat for duration. Keep the weights over the chest at all times and do not lock elbows. Keep head in alignment with spine.
C69	FB Tricep Extensions	Sit on edge of ball, hold dumbbell in right hand. Raise right arm to ceiling. Keeping right elbow still, pointing to ceiling throughout, supported by left hand, bend right arm at elbow, lowering weight to back. Straighten arm and repeat for duration. Keep head up at all times and do not lock elbows. Repeat using other arm.
C70	FB Bicep Curls	Sit on edge of ball holding a dumbbell in each hand, with arms extended palms facing up. Bend both elbows, bringing palms to shoulders. Lower to starting position. Repeat for duration. Keep back straight and head up throughout. Do not lock elbows.
C71	FB Tricep Kickbacks	Stand with left hand resting on ball, holding a dumbbell in right hand. Bend right elbow and lift right hand to top of right hip (so elbow is pointing backwards). Keeping elbow where it is, straighten arm. Bend and repeat. Repeat on both arms. Keep head in alignment with spine, and do not lock elbows.
C72	FB Advanced Press ups	Hands on centre of ball with feet on floor - hip width apart, keeping body and arms straight throughout. Lower body by bending arms. Straighten arms to raise. Repeat. Do not lock elbows and keep head in alignment with spine.
C73	FB Crunches	Lie on floor with ball as close to bottom as possible. Raise knees so thighs are at right angles to body and place lower legs on ball. Place hands on thighs, and raise shoulders off floor. Lower trunk and repeat. Keep lower back pressed into floor at all times and focus at one point on the ceiling above throughout.
C74	FB Killer Holds	Place hands on front edge of ball and feet on floor - hip width apart. Extend arms to front, pushing ball forwards and support body weight on hands and toes only. Hold position. Try to keep head aligned with spine. Advanced exercise.
C75	FB Adductors	Lie on back on floor, legs bent and feet flat on floor. Lower both knees to either side, placing ball between thighs. Keeping lower back and head pressed into the floor throughout, and using arms stretched out to side for support, squeeze knees together and then release. Repeat for duration.
C76	FB Calf Raises	Stand with feet shoulder width apart, loosen off knees. Place the ball so it is pressed against the lower back. Keep back straight and pressed against the ball at all times, raise onto toes and then lower - do not lock knees. Ball will roll up and down the back. Repeat for duration.
C77	Shoulder Press	Stand on rubber/tubing with both feet, holding each end in each hand at shoulder height. Palms can face inwards or forwards. Push hands straight up to ceiling, and then lower to starting position. Repeat for duration. Do not lock elbows and Try to keep head aligned with spine.
C78	Bicep Curl	Stand on rubber/tubing with both feet, holding each end in each hand. Extend arms with palms facing up. Bend the elbows, bringing palms to shoulders. Lower to starting position. Repeat for duration. Keep elbows fixed to ribs throughout with back straight and head up.
C79	Bench Press	Lie face up on bench, with rubber/tubing either passing under the bench or under your back. Cross the tubing in front of chest and hold the ends of the rubber/tubing in either hand. Push hands upwards towards ceiling and then return to chest. Repeat for duration. Make sure lower back and head are pressed into bench throughout and do not lock elbows.
C80	Flyes	Lie face up on bench, with rubber/tubing either passing under the bench or under your back. Cross the rubber/tubing across the body and hold the ends of the rubber/tubing in either hand. Hold so arms are straight and pointing to ceiling. Lower arms to sides so arms are out stretched and are at right angles to body. Return to starting position and repeat. Ensure lower back and head are pressed into bench at all times.
C81	Lateral Raise	Stand on rubber/tubing with both feet, holding each end in each hand, resting by thighs. Lift both arms out to side until hands are at shoulder height. Lower arms back to side. Repeat for duration. Try to keep head aligned with spine.
C82	Seated Row- lats	Sit on floor with back straight and head up. Loop rubber/tubing around the feet and hold each end in each hand. Keep elbows tight into the sides of the body and pull backwards with your elbows. Return and repeat. Do not lock elbows.
C83	Seated Row- traps	Sit on floor with back straight and head up. Loop rubber/tubing around the feet and hold each end in each hand. Lift elbows up to the side of the body and pull backwards with your elbows. Return and repeat. Do not lock elbows.
C84	Tricep Extension	Stand on rubber/tubing with both feet, holding each end in both hands. Raise arms to ceiling. Keeping both elbows still and pointing to ceiling. Bend arms at elbows, lowering to back. Straighten arms and repeat for duration. Do not lock elbows and try to keep head aligned with spine.
C85	Front Raises	Stand on rubber/tubing with both feet, holding each end in either hand with palms resting on front of thighs. Keeping arms straight and in front of body, lift alternate arms forward to shoulder height. Repeat for duration. Try to keep head aligned with spine. Keep body still - only the arms move.
C86	Single Leg Press	Lie on floor on your side. Bend lower leg and use lower arm for support. Loop rubber/tubing around the top foot and hold both ends in one hand. Pull knee into chest and then extend leg until straight. Do not lock knees. Repeat for duration. Repeat using other leg.
C87	Leg Curl	Lie face down on floor. Rubber/tubing has already been attached to wall or is being held by a partner who is kneeling behind you. Attach rubber/tubing to right foot. Bend right knee, trying to bring heel to your bottom. Lower and repeat for duration. Repeat using left leg. Your lower leg is the only body part that moves - all else remains pressed against floor throughout.
C88	Punching	Stand with rubber/tubing behind back or attached to wall behind you. You can cross the rubber/tubing in front of chest if desired. Hold each end in each hand. Punch forward with right arm, and pull it back whilst punching with the left arm. Repeat for duration. Try to keep head aligned with spine and do not lock elbows.
C89	Abductors	Loop rubber/tubing around both legs and lie on floor on your side. Bend lower leg and use lower arm for support. Raise upper leg up to side as high as possible, lower and repeat for duration. Repeat using other leg.
C90	Adductors	Lie on floor on your side. Bend lower leg and use arms for support. The rubber/ tubing has already been attached above you or is being held by a partner. Attach the rubber/tubing to the upper leg which is raised to the side. Lower the upper leg so both legs are together, raise and repeat for duration. Repeat using other leg.
C91	Toe Pushes	Sit on floor with back straight and head up. Loop rubber/tubing around the feet and hold each end in each hand. Keep elbows fixed to the side of the body and push forward with the balls of both feet. Return and repeat.